This special limited edition contains excerpts from

———————

Commentaries on the History and Cure of Diseases
by William Heberden, M.D.

first published in 1802

———————

Presented as a service to medicine
by Lederle Laboratories

EX LIBRIS

———————————

From the collection of the
Yale University
Medical Historical
Library

COMMENTARIES

ON

THE HISTORY AND CURE

OF

DISEASES.

———◆———

BY

WILLIAM HEBERDEN, M.D.

Γέρων, καὶ κάμνειν οὐκέτι δυνάμενος, τοῦτο τὸ βιβλίον ἔγραψα,
συντάξας τὰς μετὰ πολλῆς τριβῆς ἐν ταῖς τῶν ἀνθρώπων νόσοις
καταληφθείσας μοι πείρας.

ALEX. TRALL. Lib. XII.

LONDON:

PRINTED FOR T. PAYNE, MEWS-GATE;
By S. Hamilton, Falcon-Court, Fleet-Street.

1802.

PREFACE.

———————

PLUTARCH says *, that the life of a vestal vir-
gin was divided into three portions; in the first
of which she learned the duties of her profession, in the second she practised them, and in
the third she taught them to others. This is no
bad model for the life of a physician : and as I
have now passed through the two first of these
times, I am willing to employ the remainder
of my days in teaching what I know to any
of my sons who may choose the profession of
physic; and to him I desire that these papers
may be given.

The notes, from which the following observations were collected, were taken in the cham-

* Plutarch. in Numâ, et ει πρεσβυτερω πολιτευτ.

bers of the sick from themselves, or from their attendants, where several things might occasion the omission of some material circumstances. These notes were read over every month, and such facts, as tended to throw any light upon the history of a distemper, or the effects of a remedy, were entered under the title of the distemper in another book, from which were extracted all the particulars here given relating to the nature and cure of diseases. It appeared more advisable to give such facts only, as were justified by the original papers, however imperfect, than either to supply their defects from memory, except in a very few instances, or than to borrow any thing from other writers.

The collections from the notes, as well as the notes themselves, were written in Latin, the distempers being ranged alphabetically; and this is the reason that the titles are here in that language. In making the extracts it was not only more easy to follow the order in which the observations had been ranged, but there was likewise less danger of any confusion or omission; and little or no inconvenience can arise from preserving the Latin names of the distempers.

An useful addition might have been made to these papers by comparing them with the current doctrine of diseases and remedies, as also with what is laid down in practical writers, and with the accounts of those who treat of the dissections of morbid bodies; but at my advanced age it would be to no purpose to think of such an undertaking.

COMMENTARIES

ON THE HISTORY AND CURE

OF DISEASES.

CHAPTER I.

Of Diet.

MANY physicians appear to be too strict and particular in the rules of diet and regimen, which they deliver as proper to be observed by all who are solicitous either to preserve or recover their health. The too anxious attention to these rules hath often hurt those who are well, and added unnecessarily to the distresses of the sick. The common experience of mankind will sufficiently acquaint any one with the sorts of food which are wholesome to the generality of men; and his own experience will teach him which of these agrees best with his particular constitution. Scarcely any other directions beside these are wanted, except that, as variety of food at the same meal, and poignant

B

sauces, will tempt most persons to eat more than they can well digest, they ought therefore to be avoided by all who are afflicted with any chronical disorder, or wish to keep free from them. But whether meat should be boiled, or roasted, or dressed in any other plain way, and what sort of vegetables should be eaten with it, I never yet met with any person of common sense (except in an acute illness) whom I did not think much fitter to choose for himself, than I was to determine for him. Small beer, where it agrees, or water alone, are the properest liquors at meals. Wine or spirits mixed with water have gradually led on several to be sots, and have ruined more constitutions than ever were hurt by small beer from its first invention.

In fevers a little more restraint is necessary, but not so much as is often enjoined. The stronger sorts of meat and fish are most usually loathed by the sick themselves, nor could they be eaten without offending the stomach, and increasing the distemper, while it is at all considerable; but in its decline, the sick are often desirous of some of the milder sorts of meat, and no harm follows from indulging their desire. The English nation are said to eat more meat when they are well than most others; but were remarkable, so long ago as the time of Erasmus, for avoiding it more scrupulously when they are sick, than any other people. How high soever the fever be, the sick may safely be nourished with weak broths and gellies, and with any vegetable substances, if we except the acrid and aromatic, or with the infusions or decoctions prepared from them; and I know no reason for preferring any of these to the rest. Eggs and milk have been, I know not by what authority, forbidden in all fevers; but, as far as my experience goes, they both afford innocent food in the worst, where they are grateful to the patients.

The feverish thirst is best allayed by pure water, which may be drunk either warm, or cold, at the option of the sick person, and he may drink as much as he pleases; but I see no advantage in persuading him to gorge himself with liquids, as is often done, against his inclination and stomach. If water be deemed too insipid, currant gelly, and a variety of syrups, may be dissolved in it; or apples sliced or roasted, tamarinds, sage, or balm, or toasted bread, may be infused in it; or decoctions may be made of oatmeal, barley, or rice; or the water may be made into an emulsion with the oily seeds; all which with a variety of similar substances, merely correct its insipidness, but in other respects leave it just what it was.

There is scarcely any distemper, in every stage of which it may not be safely left to the patient's own choice, if he be perfectly in his senses, whether he will sit up, or keep his bed. His strength and his ease are chiefly to be attended to in settling this point; and who can tell so well as himself, what his ease requires, and what his strength will bear?

Doubts are often raised about the propriety of changing the linen in sickness, just as there have been about changing the foul air of the sick chamber by any of the means which could refresh and purify it. There can be very little reason to fear any mischief from the cold which the sick may feel while their clean linen is putting on; for their attendants, with common care, will do this as safely as many other things which must necessarily be done for them. But some have a strange opinion of harm from the smell of the soap perceivable in linen after it has been washed *, and therefore allow not their patients, when they change their linen, ever to put on fresh, but such only as has been worn, or lain in, by other persons. By this con-trivance indeed the smell of the soap might be

* Diemerbroeck de Peste, l. ii. c. 3. annot. 6.

taken off, but few cleanly people would think they gained any advantage by the change. Now, if a faint smell of soap were noxious, then soap-makers, and laundry-servants, must be remarkably unhealthy; which is contrary to experience: nor is it less so, that the sick are injured by the cleanness of what they wear; on the contrary, the removing of their foul things has often diffused over them a sense of ease and comfort, which has soon lulled them into a quiet and refreshing sleep.

CHAP. 2.

Ratio Medendi.

ONE of the first considerations in the cure of a disease is, whether it require any evacuations; that is, whether it have been the general opinion of practical authors, that emetics, cathartics, diuretics, bleeding (by leeches, cupping-glasses, or the lancet), sudorifics, blisters, issues, sternutatories, or salivation, have in similar cases been found to be beneficial.

2dly. Whether it be a distemper, for which any specific, or certain remedy, has been found out. Many such in all ages, and in every country, have been for a little while in fashion;

very few of which have justified the promises
of their patrons, and answered the wishes of
physicians and patients: so that there is no
where more reason to be upon our guard, and
to remember the old caution, νᾶφε καὶ μέμνασ'
ἀπιϛεῖν. However, the honour of this title
may be justly claimed by the Peruvian bark for
the cure of agues; quicksilver for Venereal
disorders; sulphur for the itch; and perhaps
opium for some spasms; and Bath waters for
the injury done to the stomach by drinking.

Beside the few remedies here mentioned, it may
be doubted whether ten others have upon any
good authority been reputed specifics, or certain
remedies for particular diseases, the reputation
of which has afterwards been sufficiently confirmed by experience. Borax has been cele-
brated as such for aphthæ; the Portland powder
for the gout; squills and the fetid gum-resins
for the asthma; soap-ley for the gravel and
stone; hemlock for cancers; electrification for
blindness; antimony for continual fevers; sugar
of lead for hæmorrhages; and some few others
for other distempers.

Though, among the pretended specifics, some
have very little virtue, and others may be incon-
stant in their operations; yet, if a physician be
satisfied that they are safe, there may be many

occasions when he may with propriety employ them.

3dly. Vomiting, purging, pain, and other troublesome symptoms, are in many cases so urgent, as to make some present relief indispensably requisite; for the procuring of which, opium is very commonly the most effectual means.

4thly. In long and obstinate diseases, in which no particular remedy is found to have succeeded, it is often advisable to have recourse to the general means of strongly affecting, and of making considerable changes in the state of the body; in hopes, by this shock, of dislodging the cause of the disease. For this end, mercury, antimony, hemlock, and electrification, are sometimes employed.

Lastly, where there is no room for any thing else, there it is the duty of a physician to exert himself as much as possible in supporting the powers of life, by strengthening the appetite and digestion, and by providing that the stools, and sleep, and every other article of health, shall approach as nearly as may be to its natural state.

There may be such a state of a distemper, in which the whole attention of the physician must be given up to the supporting and enli-

vening the vital powers; but there can be no
stage of any disease which does not require
some attention to this important point. As this
is a precept, in the due observance of which
the welfare of every patient is deeply interested,
it will be worth while to say something more
upon this subject.

Τὸ ἐνορμῶν—ψυχὴ—Archæus—spiritus animales—Natura—

These and various other terms have been
employed to denote the principle of life, or
that unknown energy, which makes the difference between an animated body, and an inanimate mass of matter.

In the physiology and pathology of the human body, there has been perhaps both too
much and too little use made of that vital
principle which constitutes the animal. Some
have pretended to a knowledge of it much
beyond what we have hitherto attained, and
have employed it in the ministry of the animal
œconomy, and in explaining the causes and
cures of diseases, guided much more by their
own fancies and speculations, than by the authority of facts and experience; while others,
in accounting for the same appearances, have
overlooked the laws and powers peculiar to
animal life, and have endeavoured to solve

all difficulties by the common mechanical powers, and by the general properties of dead matter.

Whatever animation be, experience has undoubtedly acquainted us with several means both of deadening, and of invigorating its operations. Of the first sort is in an eminent degree the fox-glove, and all the narcotic poisons:. to the second belong wine and spirituous liquors, all strengtheners of the stomach, aromatics, and every thing capable of irritating the senses. But vinous liquors in a certain quantity oppress, and some of the narcotics in a small dose exhilarate the powers of life.

Many of the narcotics being applied in a small wound, to any part of the surface of the body, will have their full effect in damping or destroying the vital energy; but most of them, and almost all of the opposite class, exert their powers only when taken down into the stomach; the control and dominion of which part over the principle of animation throughout the whole body are such, that universal refreshment and invigoration, or faintness and death itself, will be the instantaneous effects of its being touched by certain friendly or injurious substances.

In all distempers it is one part of the physician's duty to remove or relieve, as far as can safely be done, the present inconveniences: but the mischief principally to be dreaded in every illness is its tendency to destroy life; and against this the patient is most solicitously to be guarded. Now, of the means before mentioned by which the vires vitæ can be supported and strengthened, great irritations of the senses can only afford a momentary relief in sudden languors and faintings. Wine and aromatics will indeed make a more lasting impression on the stomach, and in many languid illnesses may be administered with great advantage; but they must be used with caution, as the vinous liquors may intoxicate, and both of them in many distempers may excite too great a degree of heat. Dr. Morton's practice in the last century has been much censured for his method of cure by an immoderate use of aromatics, for the purpose, as he says, of exciting and expanding the spiritus animales. A freer use may safely be made of the mild astringents and bitters, and there are perhaps few disorders in which they would not make very useful associates of other medi cines. Chamomile flowers in powder are sufficiently grateful to the stomach; but light infusions of the barks, and woods, and roots, are preferable to their powders. Of this very numerous class of simples a great variety of medicines may be made; but none perhaps better than an infusion made by one ounce of the Peruvian bark and one dram of the root of gentian, put into a pint of boiling water. I hardly know that distemper in which two ounces of this infusion might not be taken twice a day with safety, and, I believe, with advantage.

The Peruvian bark has been more objected to than any other of these medicines in cases of considerable inflammation, or where a free expectoration is of importance; for it is supposed to have, beyond any other stomach medicine, such a strong bracing quality, as to tighten the fibres still more which were already too much upon the stretch in an inflammation, and its astringency has been judged to be the likely means of checking or putting a stop to expectoration. All this appeared much more plausible when taught in the schools of physic, than probable when I attended to fact and experience. The unquestionable safety and acknowledged use of the bark in the worst stage of an inflammation, when it is tending to a mortification, affords a sufficient answer to the first of these objections; and I have several times seen it given plentifully in the confluent small-pox, without lessening in any degree the expectoration. An asthma, which seemed to be near its last stage, became very little trouble-some for several years, during which the patient took two scruples of the bark every morning and night. If great care be taken not to give it in such a manner as to load or oppress the stomach, every reasonable objection would, in my judgment, be removed, to the giving of it in any distemper whatever. For the purpose now under consideration, its efficacy is the same with any other bitters; but some preference may perhaps be due to this simple on account of its friendly powers to the human body, mani-fested in its being a specific remedy for intermit-tents: but if any one cannot quiet his own or his patient's apprehensions of some lurking mis-chief in the Peruvian bark, any other mild bitter* may be used for the same purpose of enabling nature to struggle successfully with the malady, by invigorating the principle of animation in the stomach. Too much attention

---

* Such as a few grains of chamomile flowers powdered in a neutral saline draught; or an aromatic confection draught may be made up with a weak infusion of quassia wood, or columbo root; or, if it be made up with any distilled water, twenty drops of the tincture of gentian, or of columbo root, may be added to each draught.

can never be paid to this very important article of a just method of treating a patient; every distemper requires it, and in many it is all that a physician can do.

It is a most alarming stage of any illness, when the stomach has so entirely lost its powers, that the person is averse from taking every thing that is offered; as if nature were conscious that the vital powers were too nearly extinguished to be recoverable by any means, and therefore all were rejected: this death of the stomach never fails to be soon succeeded by an universal loss of life.

CHAP. 3.

Abdomen.

THE abdomen has been observed to swell from various other causes besides the more common ones of a dropsy either in the belly or ovaries, of pregnancy, or scirrhi of some of the viscera, or flatulence. The hard swelled bellies of children continue too long to be owing to flatulence, and they yield too soon to purging medicines to be occasioned by scirrhi. Upon the total ceasing of the menstrua, or upon a temporary obstruction of them, the abdomen

will often be swelled, and continue so for some
months. Women not uncommonly complain
of such tumors after miscarriages, or after being brought to bed. Many of these swellings
are probably owing to some secret power of the
nerves, which they frequently exert when disturbed by several poisons. They have in
some persons been known to continue for two
or three years; and, after a violent head-ach,
the whole body has swelled, and subsided within an hour. Very large swellings, continuing
for two or three days, have been known to attend the attacks of the essera, or nettle-rash.
It has often happened to the same person to have
a tumor of the abdomen disappear upon the
sudden gushing of about a pint of water from
the uterus. In one person, whose abdomen
had been swelled for two or three years, a sudden swelling would often rise up in other parts,
as on the thighs, back, and thorax, quite up to
the neck. A tumor half as big as a child's
head would suddenly rise up in the same
patient's neck; and though the swelling of the
belly never totally disappeared, yet it would
sometimes in a morning be hardly perceivable,
and in an instant the whole abdomen would
become so distended that the skin seemed ready

to break. She often felt something move from the stomach to the limbs, which were immediately convulsed.

There often occur pains in the abdomen, similar to those which are frequently felt in the thorax, in which the viscera seem not at all concerned, but which are rather of a rheumatic nature, and will continue for a very long time. The remedies are—the volatile liniment, with, or without, the addition of laudanum; empl. cymini; a perpetual blister; an oily draught, with as much volatile salt as can easily be borne; opium; and all the rheumatic medicines.

Chap. 4.

Abortus.

One woman miscarried five-and-thirty times. Though the third month be most usually the time of miscarrying, yet there are some women who constantly miscarry about the fifth or sixth month; and in these the milk running out of their breasts is a sign of the approaching miscarriage. A woman who was with child of twins miscarried of one at the end of three months, but went on with the other, who was born at the proper time, and lived to maturity. Abortions are the effects of accidents, of

mal-conformation, and of ill health: if frequently repeated, they are also the causes of
ill health, and occasion the fluor albus, and the
whole train of evils belonging to what is called
the hysteric passion, and likewise those which
are enumerated under the article of *a broken
constitution**. One woman, after frequent abortions, took for a long time three drams of bark
in a day while she was breeding, and went her
time, and brought forth the strongest of all her
children.

CHAP. 5.

Alvus.

A VERY great difference is observable in
different constitutions in regard to the evacuation
by stool. One man never went but once in a
month : another had twelve stools every day for
thirty years, and afterwards seven in a day for
seven years, and in the mean time did not fall
away, but rather grew fat.

The fæces sometimes lie in the rectum for
many months, and are collected into a large
hard mass, which cannot be voided without the
help of a surgeon. The signs of this are, pains
in the belly; a constant desire to go to stool,

* Chap. 94.

even just after an evacuation; none but liquid fæces are ever voided; and the disorder is attended with a difficulty of making water.

The inner coat of the rectum is sometimes so relaxed as to come out after every stool, and in riding, and will not go up again without the assistance of the hand: an astringent fomentation may be applied with some advantage after every stool.

With the tape-worm, and with the ascarides, there is a most troublesome and almost intolerable itching of the fundament towards night.

Great pains are not uncommonly felt in the anus, which are sometimes relieved, but oftener exasperated, by stool, and are not unfrequently worse in bed than in the day-time, and even than in walking or riding; and in this state they will last several years. A small blister kept open upon the thigh for two or three months has cured this disorder. These pains sometimes proceed from an inflammation, and are aggravated to an almost intolerable degree by sitting, standing, coughing, sneezing, or making water. Where the inflammation has suppurated, the healing of the abscess will in some constitutions be succeeded by broken health, or by a fatal pulmonary consumption; whether it be because the disorder at first was not merely local, or because the habit of body became diseased by the too long continuance of the ulcer before it was properly opened and healed. In order to prevent these mischievous consequences, it is often advisable to open an issue as soon as the abscess begins to heal *.

CHAP. 6.

Aneurysma.

ANEURYSMATIC tumors of the neck will often continue for many years, attended with some degree of difficulty in breathing, and at last end in sudden death. Many tumors of the neck, apparently of this sort, from having a strong pulsation in them, have after several years spontaneously decreased, till at last they have almost disappeared.

CHAP. 7.

Angina, and Scarlet Fever.

THE scarlet fever begins with the common symptoms of other fevers. On the first or second day an unusual redness appears on the skin, and there is a slight pain of the throat. At the same time in some patients there are swell-

* See chap. 40, on the *Fistula Ani.*

ings under each ear, or in other glands, which are not always dispersed without coming to suppuration. In others, the arms, and particularly the fingers, have swelled; which swellings have happened indifferently, both where the disease hath proved gentle, and where it hath been fatal. On the third or fourth day the soreness of the throat goes off; about the sixth day the redness of the skin begins to retreat; and, if all things go on well, the distemper abates very fast after the seventh day.

In some of these fevers the whole skin is coloured, in others only the breast and arms; and it is not uncommon to see the redness only on the back of the wrist. This scarlet colour is either equably diffused over the whole skin, without any spots or small pimples, or is deeper coloured in some places, and lighter in others; or it is attended with little swellings, like the stinging of nettles; or else with very small eruptions, like the measles. After the redness has disappeared, the whole skin is often renewed, the old one either peeling off in large pieces, or becoming rough and branny, and so falling off. The redness of the skin affords no certain mark of the degree and event of the disorder: I have seen it become much more florid without any relief to the patient, and grow pale without any ill consequence: the warmth of the bed is so far from being always the certain means of making the eruption more florid and vigorous, that I remarked it in one patient to have been constantly faint and languid while she was in bed, and to have a far livelier hue as long as she was up.

The eruption is often attended with a very troublesome itching. It sometimes resembles the measles so exactly as not to be easily distinguished from the measley efflorescence; though this be a matter of great importance, because the method of cure in these two distempers is extremely different. The redness of the scarlet fever is more equally diffused than in the measles, and is not in distinct spots with the natural colour of the skin interposed; yet, in some few cases, I have seen it so. Then in the measles the eruption rises more above the skin, and occasions a manifest roughness to the touch, which is hardly observable in the scarlet fever, except a very little roughness sometimes in the arms. In the scarlet fever there is no cough, the eyes do not water, and the eye-lids are not red and swoln; all which rarely fail to attend the measles. The time likewise of the eruption is different; for it appears in the scarlet fever both in the face and arms on the first or second day; but in the measles it begins only on the third day of the fever to be visible about the chin, and does not come to the arms and hands till the fourth or fifth day.

Beside the restlessness and languor, which are very great in the scarlet fever, several who have it in a great degree are troubled with a sharp humour in their throats and nostrils, which makes them deaf, and hoarse, and even dumb, and takes away their senses of tasting and smelling. The inside of the nostrils and all the upper lip has been so corroded with this humour as to leave these parts sore and scabbed for a long time after the ceasing of the fever.

This distemper is not often fatal; and is sometimes so very slight as to last hardly a day, and would be utterly unnoticed, if, together with other very gentle symptoms, there were not some blush of redness perceivable in the skin, and if at the same time others of the family were not ill of this fever in a more violent manner, so as to leave no room to doubt about its nature.

There is no other distemper in which a delirium is of so little importance as in this: in other fevers it seldom comes on till they have arrived at a dangerous height; but it sometimes accompanies a scarlet fever on the very first day;

and many of these patients never fail to be light-headed every night, though, except this, there be not any unfavourable symptom from the beginning to the end of their illness.

The small-pox is not more infectious than this malady among children and very young persons of both sexes. After their twentieth year, men are very little liable to catch it, though I have seen one man in it who was four-and-thirty; but I have not unfrequently known not only the middle-aged, but even elderly women ill of this distemper: however, the older they are, the more secure they are found to be from its contagion.

This fever has begun to show itself on the fifth day after the infection was, most probably, taken by those who, being perfectly well before, have been brought to the house where some children were ill of it: and perhaps the space of time intervening between the infection and sickening may here, as well as in the small-pox, be generally nearly the same.

Where the scarlet fever proves fatal, a coma will sometimes show itself about the fifth or sixth day, or a shortness of breath with spitting of blood in those whose lungs appeared before to be sound. Some few are attacked with such violence as to die within the first three days.

After the fever is much abated, and all danger is past, the glands under the ears will sometimes swell with considerable pain, and even come to suppuration, and in some the testicles have swelled: the limbs will also be afflicted with rheumatic pains.

In the fever which has just been described, there is always some degree of redness in the skin, and the throat is not without an uneasy sensation. Where it happens that the throat is full of little ulcers attended with considerable pain, there the disease, though the skin be ever so red, is not denominated from this colour, but from the soreness of the throat, and obtains the name of the *malignant sore throat*; and many suppose that the two disorders differ in nature as well as in name: of this let the reader judge, when he has considered the histories of both.

§ 2. *The Malignant Sore Throat.*

It is matter of doubt whether, in some instances of the malignant sore throat, the fever, or the aphthous ulcers, come first. For it is observable that on the very first day of the fever the fauces will sometimes appear so much loaded with them, as to make it improbable that they should all have come on and arrived at the state in which they appear within the space of one day. It is by no means unlikely that the patients should pay very little attention to these small sores; for they seem to occasion very little pain, far less than what is felt in a very slight inflammatory sore throat; and there is either no difficulty of swallowing, or, however, much less than one would imagine by seeing the condition of the throat. In the places where the ulcers are about to appear, the cuticle becomes whiter or ash-coloured; and when it is either rubbed off, or cracks of itself, a small ulcer is discovered without any pus. Not only as much of the fauces as can be seen, but the inside likewise of the nostrils, seems to be the seat of these ulcers. All these parts will be swelled when the sores are numerous, deep, and sordid; whence the patient becomes hoarse, and almost dumb. The external part of the throat, and the whole face, will also be sometimes swelled.

I have seen the whole skin intensely red on the very first day of the distemper: at other times only the breast and arms have had this colour; in some patients it has not been observable until the fourth day of the fever, and in many it is scarcely or never perceived at all. Where this redness was the most florid, the patients have not seemed at all the better; nor have they been apparently hurt when it has faded and disappeared.

Some judgment may be formed of the danger of the fever from the appearance of the aphthæ; for that will be greater in proportion as these occupy a larger space, and are deeper and more firmly fixed, and oftener grow again, and are of a more gangrenous hue. But the condition of these sores, though it be an index, yet is by no means the cause of the danger: for the enfeebled and disordered state of all the functions of the body, evidently points out such a malignity of the fever, as cannot be owing to the affection of the uvula, or tonsils, which in other distempers we often see ulcered, and eaten away, without any danger of the patient's life. These sores therefore, like pestilential buboes, point out the nature of the disorder; but the danger arises not from them, but from the fever.

This distemper is sometimes so slight as to require no remedies, and sometimes so violent as to admit of no relief. Several become lightheaded on the second day of the fever, or comatose, breathing with great difficulty, and bending back their heads as far as they can; a purulent and offensive mucus flows from their nostrils, their throats appear gangrenous, and these symptoms are soon followed by death: while others, after having shown some little appearances of this distemper for a day or two, recover without any assistance. But most of those who are afflicted with this fever are very ill for six or seven days before they show any signs of amendment. While it continues, a remarkable flow of saliva often runs out of their mouths.

The languor, feebleness, and inquietude, are greater than might be expected from the apparent degree of fever. Where it proves fatal, the anxiety increases, and together with the coma, difficulty of breathing, and offensive mucus before mentioned, there is also an averseness from taking every kind of nourishment or drink. This happens not because they are unable to swallow, for I have often wondered to see how readily they could do this when they would try, though the fauces seemed full of sordid ulcers, and their breath could hardly be fetched. The trachea indeed seems to be the seat of these ulcers, rather than the œsophagus.

Among the rarer symptoms may be reckoned a profuse bleeding of the nose. I have likewise observed this disease to have been succeeded by rheumatic pains, and swellings. Some persons, though this very rarely happens, have been infected with it more than once.

The malignant sore throat may justly be called the distemper of childhood and youth in males. Among many patients whom I have seen in this fever, I do not remember above two or three males who were past twenty, and only one who was more than thirty. Women are never entirely secure from it at any age, though the older they are, they are found to be the less apt to take the infection. The younger the patients are, the greater is their danger; which is contrary to what happens in the measles and small-pox. In a child who died on the sixth day of this distemper, and was opened, the velum pendulum was putrid; the tonsils were outwardly blackish, and livid within; the uvula was covered with a thick mucus resembling a membrane; the epiglottis was sound, and so was the œsophagus: but that mucous covering descended down the trachea quite to its division, in the upper part of which it appeared like a membrane, in the lower part it was more like mucus.

From the foregoing description of the scarlet fever and malignant sore throat, it seems highly probable that they are both names of the same distemper, with some little variety in a few of the symptoms; and this opinion is confirmed by our finding that they are both epidemical at the same time. Even in the same family, where a number of children have been ill either together, or immediately after one another, some have had the distinguishing symptoms of the scarlet fever, and others of the malignant sore throat. But the solution of this question is of very little importance; for, let the distempers be ever so different, the method of cure in both is exactly the same, except only what may be thought necessary to be applied to the ulcers of the throat.

There may be more use in determining, whether this fever, like the small-pox, be incapable of infecting the same person more than once. According to my experience, some children have beyond all doubt been afflicted a second time with this disease: but it is evident that this happens very seldom; for otherwise, in such a common distemper, there could be no more question about the possibility of a second infection, than there is in the itch, or in Venereal disorders. I have met with several grown persons who have had frequent returns of a slight sore throat, which at these times was beset with little ulcers similar to those of the malignant sore throat, but without any, or, at most, without much fever, and without any disco‑louring of the skin. If this slight angina bear any relation to the malignant one, it is not more than subsists between the small-pox and those eruptions which are sometimes observable in such as have already had that disease, while they are nursing and attending others who are ill of it.

The very different nature of the malignant from that of the inflammatory sore throat, toge‑ther with the tender age and weak habit of those who are most subject to it, have made physicians at present very generally agree to condemn bleeding, as what would be useless at best, and often hurtful to such patients. Yet in some few persons, whose strength seemed able to bear it, and whose heat, and head-ach, and manner of living, seemed to require it, I have known blood taken away once, and even twice, in the beginning of the distemper, with safety, and perhaps with advantage. All pur‑ging medicines should be avoided till towards the end of the fever; and if a spontaneous diarrhœa come on, it should be checked as soon as possible. Blisters are peculiarly ser‑viceable, and the patient should never be with‑out one, or more, until he be out of danger. Decoctions or infusions of the Peruvian bark, joined with aromatics, appear to be the most

useful medicines; and equal parts of a decoction of the bark and of the pectoral decoction
make a very good gargle. This gargle may
be injected with a syringe into the throats of
children: but this should by no means be
done so often as to tease or fatigue them; for
the advantage of doing this does not seem to
me to be very great above that of getting them
frequently to wash their throats by drinking
either this, or some more grateful liquor. Similar reasons would forbid us still more strongly
to take great pains in rubbing off the sloughs
from these ulcers, or in scarifying them. Besides, in dangerous cases, the trachea and the
nostrils are equally the seat of these foul
ulcers, to the first of which nothing can be
applied; and if the noses of children were to
be syringed, they would swallow whatever was
washed from the nose into the stomach, where
it would not improbably do more mischief,
than in the place from which it had been removed. My only reason for suspecting that I
ought to lay more stress upon applications
made immediately to the throat, than I have
here done, is, that several physicians of deservedly great authority have judged them to be
of more importance than they have appeared
to me.

Chap. 8.

Aphthæ.

Aphthæ are found chiefly in children, and old persons, and in tedious fevers. They are usually accompanied with a soreness of the throat, some difficulty of swallowing, and apparently of bringing up phlegm, (for which they mistake the aphthæ), a hoarseness, and hiccup. The Peruvian bark is given safely in aphthous fevers, and perhaps advantageously.

Besides the aphthæ which accompany acute fevers in weak constitutions, there are some which may be called chronical: these will sometimes be very troublesome to the mouth, not only for months, but even years, without fever, or any other considerable complaint. Such aphthæ have continued for three years after a slight palsy of the face. The West-Indians sometimes bring this disorder with them into England; and they have told me that it is a very common one in those islands, and sometimes ends in a fatal diarrhœa, or dysentery. The aphthæ are supposed not only to infest the mouth and fauces, but to be continued down through the whole intestinal canal. In two who died of a lingering fever, and whose mouths were covered with aphthæ, which hung in rags all over it, there was not the least trace of them that could be found in dissection beyond the fauces.

Chap. 27.

Diarrhœa.

A DIARRHŒA arises from a variety of causes, most of which are void of all danger, and are easily removed. It is often brought on by that power, which is exerted in every part of the body, of freeing itself from any thing painful and oppressive. Not only the mischief from the noxious qualities, and improper quantities of what has been taken, and immediately offends the stomach, are carried off by means of a diarrhœa, but likewise many disorders of remote parts, or of the whole body, (such as morbid impressions from the causes of epidemical complaints, and of fevers) are by the self-correcting powers of an animal body determined to the bowels, and thence discharged by a diarrhœa.

* A young man, who had laboured under a true diabetes for twelve months, was seized with an acute fever, and died. The body, which was carefully examined, shewed no marks of disease. The kidneys were imagined to be rather fuller of blood than usual; and the gall-bladder was perfectly empty.—*E.*

The observation of this has given occasion to that useful caution of not being too hasty in stopping a recent spontaneous purging, it being frequently useful to co-operate with nature in promoting this evacuation. For this purpose rhubarb has been chiefly recommended, and deservedly; but instead of rhubarb I have many times given two or three drams of the neutral purging salts, and think they have always done as well, and in some cases better, by making a more speedy and complete evacuation of what had offended the bowels, and with less sickness. An emetic is also successfully used where the nausea is very great; but otherwise I think a vomit is unnecessary. Fifteen grains of powdered ipecacuanha, or even half a pint of carduus or chamomile-flower tea, will sufficiently answer this purpose.

After what had oppressed the bowels has been removed, a weak or too irritable a state of them may still continue: hence arise indigestions, flatulence, heartburn, frequent returns of the diarrhœa, and a predominant acid in the stomach. The testaceous powders and chalk julep are the proper correctors of this too ready acescence of the humours; which therefore should be employed: but they will not alone be of much avail in stopping a diarrhœa which is considerable enough to require any medicines at all. Nutmeg, cinnamon, pomegranate bark, and many other astringent vegetable substances, are much more efficacious, but yet often require to be joined with remedies which sooth the too great irritableness of the intestines, namely gum-arabic, starch, and opiates. Half a dram of testaceous powder, fifteen grains of pomegranate bark, and half a scruple of nutmeg, with three drops of tincture of opium, may be taken in any distilled, or common water, once or twice a day in the more chronical and habitual purgings, or once in six hours in the more recent and violent ones. Tinctura opii mixed in any pleasant julep, so as to let the patient take as much as contains three or four drops after every purging stool, is in many cases required; and beside this manner of giving the opium, it is often extremely serviceable to give from twenty to forty drops in a quarter of a pint of mucilage of quince seeds, or of starch, administered in a clyster. Gum-arabic dissolved in water, or in milk and water, may be taken to the quantity of one ounce in twenty-four hours: and, lastly, one large spoonful of clean mutton fat, mixed with a quarter of a pint of milk hot enough to melt the fat, and drunk twice a day, is not only a good remedy, but nourishing food.

This method has appeared to me the most effectual, where the diarrhœa was curable and needed to be cured; but there are instances of its being habitual and harmless, at least for several years, and returning upon the slightest occasions for the greatest part of a person's life. I have seen an instance of a diarrhœa's continuing for three months at the rate of twenty times in a day, without any apparent injury to the health. In such cases it is difficult, and perhaps hardly desirable, to effect a cure of what is not so much a distemper, as an inconvenience, which may be more than compensated by the benefit which it does to the general habit of the body. Where the appetite fails, and the flesh wastes, no time should be lost in checking the purging; but if neither of these be affected, a cautious delay, and gentle remedies, will prove the best means of restoring the patient.

Among the many causes of diarrhœas, there are some, though few in proportion to the others, which are neither to be checked by the milder, nor subdued by the more vigorous methods of cure, but end only in the patient's death, after having been in vain opposed, as is usual in desperate cases, by a variety of regular and irregular practitioners. In some of these the glands of the mesentery and intestines have been found scirrhous; in others, though they were opened, and all the parts examined by the most experienced and dexterous anatomists, the stomach and bowels have appeared in a natural state, and no cause of the distemper could be discovered. I have not mentioned a sea voyage, nor the Bath, because I have known them fail so often, that I have no encouragement to depend upon them; and rather think, where they have been supposed to be successful, that the success was in reality owing to other causes.

CHAP. 28.

Digitorum Nodi.

WHAT are those little hard knobs, about the size of a small pea, which are frequently seen upon the fingers, particularly a little below the top, near the joint? They have no connexion with the gout, being found in persons who never had it: they continue for life; and being hardly ever attended with pain, or disposed to become sores, are rather unsightly, than inconvenient, though they must be some little hindrance to the free use of the fingers.

CHAP. 29.

Dolor.

PAIN is a symptom attending upon a variety of disorders, and is sometimes itself the whole distemper. It is distinguished sometimes by being periodical; sometimes it has a particular name from the part which is frequently its seat; as head-ach, hemicrania, lumbago. All other parts of the body, which have any sense of feeling, are necessarily liable to pain, though they be not so frequently molested as that the pain should be ranked as a distinct species with a particular name. Accordingly, there is no part of the body, or limbs, in which I have not observed a troublesome and lasting pain without any discolouring, or swelling, or tendency to inflammation. It will remain fixed in the same place not only for months, but frequently from one to ten years; and I have known such a pain complained of for fifteen, sixteen, seventeen, twenty-four, and even thirty years.

The more lasting of these pains are, as might be expected, moderate in degree: how-

ever, a few have continued for years, and yet
at times have raged with a vehemence
scarcely to be endured. Both sexes are subject to them, but women much oftener than
men, and particularly the very young, and the
infirm, and the pregnant. The thorax and
hypochondria are the parts which most frequently suffer from them; and though some
of these uneasy sensations may arise from internal disorders, yet in many instances there
has been no reason to suspect that the lungs,
or liver, or any other of the viscera, had the
least share in producing them. In most of
these patients the pains could not be traced up
to any certain cause; but in several they have
apparently arisen from terror, grief, and anxiety, and have unquestionably been recall-
ed and exasperated by some disturbance of
mind.

In several instances no sort of relief has
been obtained from the cold bath, fomentations, liniments with or without tinctura opii,
warm plasters, blisters, cupping, vomiting,
purging, sudorifics: setons, and even a spontaneous abscess near the part affected has failed of doing good; Bath, and sea voyages, have
proved equally unsuccessful. It is probable
that no great hurt is done to the seat of this
pain, since it has continued so long without

causing any swelling or change of colour; and yet I have once or twice known such ill-conditioned boils, and such a tendency to a mortification, follow the use of a blister, as if the part was far from being in a perfectly sound state; though there were no manifest signs of its being otherwise, except the pain. The means which have the seldomest failed, and have in some cases evidently contributed to the cure, are cold-bathing, small perpetual blisters, or (if there be objections to blisters) emplastrum cymini worn for a long time. The most powerful internal medicine is tinctura opii, from ten drops to thirty given at night alone, or, as many choose to give it, either in a spoonful of lac ammoniacum, or with a quarter of a grain of emetic tartar. The extract of hemlock has now and then appeared to weaken the cause of these obstinate ails. Cupping has sometimes succeeded; but all other bleeding, together with emetics, and cathartics, have generally proved at least useless.

Beside the pains which are either constantly felt, or rage at uncertain times, there are others which are regularly intermittent, the fits of which return as periodically as those of an ague: such I have known in the bowels, stomach, breast, loins, arms, and hips, though it be but seldom that these parts suffer in this manner; but the head and face are frequently afflicted with a periodical pain, which by its violence and duration is not the least of the maladies which embitter human life: of these some account will be found under the article of *Capitis Dolores intermittentes.*

CHAP. 30.

Dolores vagi.

WANDERING pains are near akin to the rheumatism, but may be distinguished from it by their being accompanied neither with swelling, nor any discolouring of the skin. Are they not chiefly suffered by those, whose muscular fibres have been weakened, strained, or stiffened, by long illnesses, profuse bleedings, bruises, irregular living, hard working, or the advances of age? They usually continue for many years without other ill consequences than becoming gradually a little more troublesome; but, in a very few, the parts principally affected have their power of motion more and more lessened, till at last it be quite lost. Time, and warm bathing, and flannel, may contribute a little to the cure, or relief, or however to checking the progress of these ails; and there are scarcely any other helps to be given.

CHAP. 31.

Dysenteria.

THE Dysentery is common in camps, but does not often infest those who live in healthy places with the conveniences of life about them, except at certain seasons, when it becomes epidemical, particularly among children, old women, and infirm men, and it is then fatal to many. The distinguishing symptoms of it are a frequent want of going to stool, with excessive pain, and the voiding without any relief a very little inodorous mucus, often tinged with blood, and sometimes pure blood; a pain just under the navel, together with a fever, and great loss of appetite, sleep, and strength, and sometimes a vomiting.

Since this distemper is commonly bred in camps by foul air, and is in some degree contagious (yet I have seldom seen two dysenteric persons in the same house), too great care cannot be taken in regard to cleanliness and fresh air, both for the sake of the patient and his attendants. The usual methods of treating this malady with which I was acquainted often failed of procuring ease, and of preventing its ending fatally in a sphacelus of the bowels. It appeared that in a dysentery some hurtful humours had been deposited in the intestines, which threw them into such disorderly agitations as to hinder the expulsion of what had offended them. The readiness with which the neutral salts (especially the cathartic salt) purge, their power of controlling and quieting the irregular motions of the bowels, and their aptness to stay upon the stomach without being vomited up, made me conceive hopes that they would make a valuable addition to the anti-dysenteric medicines. At first I gave only one dram every six hours, which evidently soothed the pains very soon, and before it had any effect as a purge. In other cases larger quantities were given, and with the double good effect both of affording present ease, and afterwards of entirely removing by effectual evacuations the cause of the disorder.

After the danger of the distemper is past, the patient will still be teased with a tenesmus as long as any soreness or extraordinary tenderness of the rectum remains; in which case a clyster of half a pint of fat mutton broth and twenty drops of tinctura Thebaïca scarcely ever fails of proving a cure; and it is almost the only stage of the illness in which opium is either useful or safe: if it were given in the beginning to quiet the pain before any evacuation had been made, I apprehend it would be very prejudicial.

Where this distemper has ended fatally, it has been attended with a hiccup, and a fetid water voided by stool.

Chap. 32.

Ebrietas.

THE effects of hard drinking are, flatulence, loss of appetite, morning sickness, wasting of the flesh and strength, tremblings, pains of the stomach, cough, jaundice, dropsy, forgetfulness and inattention, giddiness, diarrhœa, broken sleep.

If remedies be applied in time, and the habit of drinking can be broken, much may be hoped for in restoring the health. It is generally a favourable circumstance to have an illness arise from an external cause, rather than from any internal failing. Men of a strong constitution and high health are those who most usually indulge themselves in this excess; and these circumstances, which betrayed them into their danger, will greatly assist in helping them out.

Bath water seems specifically efficacious in curing these complaints, if applied to in time, before the liver and stomach are too deeply hurt. Nor is Bath only a remedy against the mischief which has been already done; but it is also singularly useful in preventing a relapse, by enabling the patients to correct the habit of drinking: for the nature of this water is so friendly in warming and comforting the stomach, as to relieve all that coldness and anxiety, which almost irresistibly force a hard drinker to fly to strong liquors for ease under these insufferable sensations. Warm aperient medicines occasionally used so as to prevent costiveness, if there be a disposition that way, and bitters, are the whole of what is further necessary to establish the health.

CHAP. 38.

Febris Intermittens.

THE fit of an intermittent fever seldom lasts above twenty hours, and not often so long. The shivering, and sense of coldness, with which it begins, will continue from half an hour to two hours; then succeed the heat, and restlessness; and these yield to a sweat, the degrees of which, and duration, are very various, accord-

ing as they are more or less promoted by lying in bed and drinking warm liquors. The fit will be a quotidian, returning every day; or a tertian, and return every other day; and if there be the interval of two days between the fits, it is called a quartan. Much longer intervals have been known; but these happen so seldom, that they have been distinguished by no name, and are not of any importance to deserve our notice.

Besides the common appearances of fever, every fit has been sometimes accompanied with other complaints; in some with rheumatic pains; in several with a light delirium; in others with an eruption of the skin, or colic, or faintings, with a pain and swelling of the testicles, a languidness, and almost paralytic weakness of the limbs. These have regularly come and gone with the fever, and with the cure of that have finally disappeared.

It is a question, or rather perhaps it was a question before men knew well how to cure an intermittent, whether they might safely attempt to cure it. For it was supposed to be an effort of the body to relieve itself from some latent seeds of mischief, which would shew themselves if the intermittent were cured. Some respectable names in physic have patronised this opinion, and I began to practise with a persuasion of its truth: but every year's experience weakened my belief of this doctrine, and I have long since, by numberless proofs, been convinced of the safety of stopping this fever as soon as possible: nor can I doubt of having observed ill consequences where the fever has been suffered to remain, by delaying to use the effectual means of preventing its returns. The Peruvian bark is the well-known specific, with which Providence has blessed us for the cure of this disorder; and if the first fit have been marked so clearly, as to leave no doubt of its being a genuine intermittent, this remedy should be immediately given in such a manner, as to prevent, if possible, a second. If six drams of powdered bark can be got down, by taking a dram at a time, before the hour of its return, the patient will find the fever at least much weakened, if not entirely removed; and the same quantity taken four times a day for six days will usually free the patient from all danger of a relapse. But if this medicine be not uncommonly disgustful, there may good arise, but there can be no harm, from his taking it twice a day for ten days longer. This way of using the bark I think is the most to be depended upon; but where the bark in substance cannot be taken, or borne, there two ounces of a strong decoction used as often will generally be successful. The success would be made less uncertain, if there were no objection from the patient's palate, or stomach, to the dissolving in each dose one scruple or half a dram of the extract. Bark is a difficult medicine to be got down children's throats, especially in such quantities as would cure their agues. One scruple of the extract, and as much sugar, first mixed with half a spoonful of water, and then with a spoonful and a half of milk, is a form which will disguise its nauseousness sufficiently for many children to take it without any unwillingness. But wherever either in them, or in adults, it cannot be taken or borne in any form upon the stomach, they may still have the benefit of it by having three or four ounces of the decoction with one or two drams of the powder injected at least twice a day as a clyster; and if this should not readily be retained, ten drops of tincture of opium may be added. It has been proposed to cure an intermittent by keeping the feet immersed in a strong decoction of bark: this I have known tried without success. Cases sometimes occur in which the bark, though properly taken, will not hinder the returns of the fever: this is suspected to be owing to a foulness of the stomach, which hinders the bark from making a due impression upon it; and therefore an emetic is given, and afterwards the bark is repeated as at first. If it still fail, a scruple of chamomile flowers powdered may be given in the same manner as the bark, and I have known this method more than once succeed: I have also given in some extraordinary cases two scruples of calamus aromaticus, and have found it more efficacious than a variety of other means which had been previously directed. Sometimes it has been of use to take twenty drops of tincture of opium when the fit is coming on.

A quartan ague is far more obstinate than a quotidian, or tertian, and will for a long time elude the power of the bark given in the usual manner, and all other remedies. I have found several of the inveterate quartans yield to a quarter of an ounce of the bark taken just before the coming on of the fit. From a persuasion that the bark is dangerous, if taken before the fever has perfectly subsided, many begin to take it with very uneasy apprehensions, and sometimes will too long delay taking it, to their great detriment. Now the only harm which I believe would follow from taking the bark even in the middle of the fit, is, that it might occasion a sickness, and might harass the patient by being vomited up, and might set him against it; but in my judgment it can never be taken too soon after the fever begins to decline, provided the stomach will bear it.

Chap. 39.

Febris Hectica.

A HECTIC fever is frequently mentioned in the writings of physicians, and likewise in common conversation; but the precise meaning of the term hectic has not been well settled, and generally acknowledged; so that probably, by different authors, it is not always used to express the same illness. I understand by it that fever which passes under the name of the irregular intermittent, or symptomatic, and what usually attends great suppurations; of which it may not be useless to give a short description, with some mention of the causes by which it is brought on.

This fever very much resembles the true intermittent, from which it must be carefully distinguished; for their nature is totally different, requiring a very different treatment, and thé two distempers are extremely unlike in the degree of danger with which they are attended.

In the intermittent the fits are longer, and the three stages of cold, and heat, and perspiration, are more exactly defined, and in all the fits continue nearly the same length of time; after which there is a perfect cessation of the fever. But in the clearest remissions of the hectic there is still some quickness of the pulse, so as to beat at least ten strokes more in a minute than it should in a healthy state. The fits also of the hectic vary from one another, seldom continuing to return in the same manner for more than three times together. The shivering is sometimes succeeded immediately by perspiration, without any intervening heat; sometimes it begins with heat, without any preceding cold; and the patients sometimes experience the usual chilliness without any following heat or sweat. The fit therefore of the hectic is usually shorter, not only because the whole three stages are shorter, but because one of them is often wanted, and sometimes even two.

The hectic patient is very little, or not at all relieved by the breaking out of the sweat; but is often as restless and uneasy after he begins to perspire, as he was while he shivered, or burned. All the signs of fever are sometimes found the same after the perspiration is over; and during their height the chilliness will in some patients return, which is an infallible character of this disorder. Almost all other fevers begin with a sense of cold; but in them it is never known to return and to last twenty minutes, or half an hour, while the fever seems at its height; which in the hectic will sometimes happen.

However, it is not very unusual for the hectic to have two fits, and even three, as exactly resembling one another, as those of a genuine intermittent; but afterwards they never fail to become totally irregular; so that I hardly remember an instance in which the returns continued regular for four successive fits.

The hectic in some cases comes on so seldom, and is so slight, as scarcely to be perceivable for ten or twelve days; but in other instances, where the primary disorder is very great, the fever will be strongly marked, and will attack the patient several times on the same day, so that the chilliness of a new fit will begin as soon as the perspiration of the former is ended. Several little threatenings of a cold fit have been known to return within a few hours.

In a regular intermittent, the urine during the fever is pale, and thick in the intervals; but its appearance in the hectic is governed by no rules; so that it will be either clear, or loaded, equally during the fits and in the intervals; or even muddy in the fever, and clear in its absence; and will now and then, as in common fevers, be pale during the attack, and muddy afterwards.

Beside the usual distress of a fever, the hectic patient is often harassed with pains like those of the rheumatism, which either wander through the whole body, or remain constant and fixed in one part; and, what is rather strange, often at a great distance from the primary malady, and in appearance unconnected with it. These pains have been so great, as to make no small part of the patient's sufferings, and to be not tolerable without the assistance of opium. They are chiefly observable, as far as I can judge, in those whose hectic has been occasioned by ulcers in the external parts, as in cancers of the face and breast, and in other places open to the outward air. In some few hectic cases it is remarkable that considerable tumors will instantly arise upon the limbs, or body, lasting only for a few hours, without pain, or hardness, or discolouring of the skin.

There have been those who when they thought themselves tolerably well have suddenly and vehemently been seized with a fever, not unlike an inflammatory one; and, like that, seeming very soon to bring the life into danger. However, after a few days, the distemper has abated, and the patients have had hopes of a speedy recovery: but these hopes have not improved upon them; for though the first commotions have subsided, and but little fever remain, yet this little, being kept up by some deep and dangerous cause, resists all remedies, and gradually undermining the health, ends only in death. But this is one of the rarer forms of this malady; for in the beginning it most usually dissembles its strength, making its approaches so slowly, that the sufferers feel themselves indeed not quite well, but yet for some months hardly think themselves in earnest ill; for they complain only of a slight lassitude, and that their strength and appetite are a little impaired. This state of their health may be judged not very alarming; but yet if at the same time the pulse be found half as quick again as it should be, there will be great reason for solicitude about the event. There are not many diseases in which an attention to the pulse affords more instruction than it does in this; yet even here, whoever relies too confidently and entirely upon the state of the pulse, will in some cases find himself misled: for it happens, as well as I can guess, to one among twenty hectic patients, that while all the powers of life are daily declining, with every sign of an incurable mischief, the artery will to the last minute continue to beat as quietly, and as regularly, as it ought to do in perfect health.

Great suppurations in any part of the body will bring on this fever; and it will particularly attend a scirrhous gland, while it is yet very little inflamed, and in the very beginning of the inflammation. It increases in proportion as the gland becomes more inflamed, or ulcerous, or more disposed to a gangrene. Glandular diseases are of such a nature, that some patients will linger in them, not only for many months, but even for a few years.

When a scirrhous inflammation is in any external part, and obvious to the sight, or touch, or when its seat is in the lungs, or in any of the viscera, whose functions are well known and cannot be disordered without shewing manifest signs of the disease, in all such cases we can be at no loss about the cause of the fever. But if an internal part, the uses of which are not clearly known, happen, by being diseased, to bring on hectic symptoms, there the fever, which is only symptomatic, may be mistaken for the original and only distemper.

Lying-in women, on account of the mischief arising from difficult births, are liable to this fever, and it often proves fatal. The female sex in general, after they have arrived at their fiftieth year, are in some danger of falling into this irregular intermittent: 'for in that change which their constitution experiences about this time, the glands of the womb, or ovaries, or of the breasts, are apt to become scirrhous, and as soon as they begin to inflame, the hectic comes on; and not only these, but all the glandular parts of the abdomen, seem at this time particularly liable to be diseased, and to bring on this, of which we are speaking, as well as all other signs of a ruined constitution. The same evils are the portion of hard drinkers, arising from the scirrhous state of the liver in particular, and often of the stomach, and other viscera, which are the well-known effects of an intemperate use of wine and spirituous liquors.

The slightest wound from a sharp instrument

has been the cause of many distressful symptoms, and such as have even proved fatal. For after such an accident, not only the wounded part has been in pain and has swelled, but other parts of the body, and those at a great distance from the wound, have been affected with pain and swelling, and have shown some tendency to suppuration. These symptoms never fail to be joined by the irregularly intermittent fever, which continues as long as any of them remain. The time of their continuance is uncertain: some have been harassed with them for two or three weeks; and others for as many months; and, in a few, they have ended only in death.

The hectic fever is never less formidable, than when it is occasioned by a well-conditioned suppuration, in which all the injured parts are resolved into matter so circumstanced as to be readily discharged from the body.

Inflammations of scirrhous glands in the breasts, or in the interior parts, sometimes yield to remedies, or to nature, and together with their cure, the fever, which depended upon them, ceases. But these diseased glands much oftener end in cancers and gangrenes; and the fever continues as long as any life remains.

It cannot be supposed, that a fever arising

from so many different causes, and attended with a great variety of symptoms, should always require, or bear to be treated in the same manner.

As the hectic is always occasioned by some other disease, whatever most effectually relieves the primary malady must be the best means of relieving all its natural attendants. When the fever has been the consequence of some small wound, a mixture of opium and asafœtida will prove an useful remedy. In almost all other cases, the attention of the physician must be chiefly, if not wholly employed, in removing the urgent symptoms. A cooling regimen will temper the heat, when it is excessive; the bowels must be kept nearer to a lax than a costive state; sleep, if wanted, must be procured by opium; profuse sweats may be moderated by a decoction of bark and elixir of vitriol; beside which, the greatest care must be taken that the air, and food, and exercise, may be all such, as will be most conducive to putting the body into the best general health. After doing this, the whole hope must be placed in that power, with which all animals are endowed, not only of preserving themselves in health, but likewise of correcting many deviations from their natural state. And in some happy constitutions this power has been known to exert itself successfully, in cases that have appeared all but desperate. For some patients have recovered from this fever, after there had appeared very great signs of its arising from some viscus incurably diseased, where every assistance from medicine had been tried in vain, and where the strength and flesh were so exhausted, as to leave no hopes of any help from nature. In this deplorable state, a swelling has been known to arise, which, though not far from the seat of the primary disorder, yet could not be found to have any immediate communication with it. This tumour has at length suppurated, in consequence of which the pulse has grown calmer, some degree of appetite has returned, and all appearances of distemper have gradually lessened, till the strength and health were perfectly restored. What in some very few instances I had observed nature thus to effect, I have endeavoured to imitate, by applying a blister, or by opening an issue, or seton, near the apparent seat of the internal mischief; but the success has not answered my expectations.

Not many years ago, in some fortunate recoveries from mortifications, the Peruvian bark had been prescribed, and had the credit of the cure; since which time it has been very generally used by practitioners in all tendencies to gangrenes, and where suppurations had not proceeded in a kindly manner. There is every reason to believe, that it may safely be employed in such cases; and no other remedy is known, which has any pretence to rival it for these purposes. Besides, as the hectic fever is so very like an intermittent, even where there was no suspicion of any gangrene or ulcer, the desires of the sick, or of their friends, for trying the bark, have been too importunate to be controlled; and physicians have sometimes prescribed it from their own judgment. But it has greatly disappointed all expectations of benefit to hectic patients; for it seems to have no efficacy, where there is no ulcer; and indeed it has so often been useless in mortifications, that there may be some doubt, whether in the prosperous cases the cure were not owing to other causes.

But though I dare not be confident that the Peruvian bark has any extraordinary virtues in stopping the progress of mortifications; yet I can have no doubt that it may safely be used: for neither in these cases, nor in any other, have I ever had reason to suspect its doing harm, unless it can be said to do so when it occasions a sickness or diarrhœa, where the stomach happens to be weak, or the dose has been too great, or where it has been taken in hard boluses, which were not readily dissolved in the stomach : and I remember to have heard Sir Edward Hulse say the same, who had for above forty years been giving as much of it as any physician in England, and probably much more than any one had given in all the other countries of Europe. Experience every day more and more confirms this testimony in favour of the bark : and hence it must have happened, that the quantity of it used in England for the last ten years, is ten times greater than it was in the same length of time in the beginning of the eighteenth century. It is evident therefore that the more we know of this noble simple, the less reason we find for those suspicions with which it was at first calumniated ; so that it affords some exception to the general rule, *ubi virtus, ibi virus.* Yet we are told, that many physicians are still afraid of ever giving it in the beginning of an intermittent; and some are afraid of ever curing it at all with this remedy. They may perhaps adhere to the doctrine (which I believe is founded in error), that an intermittent is an effort of nature, by which the constitution frees itself from many hurtful humours, and

from the rudiments of many impending diseases; and consequently where these friendly
exertions are checked, those dangerous maladies will fall upon the internal parts, terminating in fatal dropsies. I suspect these ground-
less fears have had their origin from those
fevers, which were falsely judged to be intermittent, when in reality they were hectic;
and that the obstructions in the abdominal
viscera were not owing to the bark, but were
the original cause of the illness.

In all chronical disorders which yield to no
other remedies, it is usual for the sick to be
urged by their own hopes, and by the advice
of their friends, to make trial of the Bath
waters. Now the inconveniences of travelling,
and of missing the comforts of their own
houses, must occasion some additional sufferings to the sick; and for these the hectic
patients can have no just hopes of having any
amends made them by going to Bath: on the
contrary, those waters would not fail, by
heightening the fever, to aggravate all their
complaints, and to hasten their death.

CHAP. 40.

Fistula Ani.

FISTULA ani, scirrhi, and ulcers of the rectum, are often attended with griping pains, tenesmus, a want and difficulty of making water, a difficulty of retaining the stools, mucous and bloody stools, the stools always loose, or not round but flatted, shiverings, a swelling, and sometimes a gangrene of the testicles, flying pains, and sometimes very acute and fixed ones in a distant part of the limbs.

The ulcers which are formed in the rectum near the sphincter ani are often neglected, upon a supposition that they are only piles; though the pain of the previous inflammation be far greater, and much more increased by coughing and sneezing. Even after the suppuration has been made, and the ulcer is broken, the discharge from it, if not great, will still be undistinguished from the piles; for a moisture has for a considerable time continued to ooze out from them, where experienced surgeons upon examination have not been able to find any ulcer. However, where the pain is excessive, or there is any purulent discharge, the opinion of a surgeon is indispensably necessary; for, if there be an inflammation or ulcer, the whole care of it belongs to him, and the sooner he is employed, the better it will be for the patient. A timely use of the proper means may hinder the forming of deep sinuses, which cannot perhaps ever be brought to a healing condition, or not without a much more painful operation than the cure would at first have cost.

Fistulous sores of the rectum will remain unhealed, and keep discharging like a fontanel for a long time: one has done so for more than thirty years. In some constitutions a previous unhealthiness may make a deposit upon the intestine; in others perhaps a neglected ulcer, arising from slight, and merely local causes, may in time taint the whole body. Whether then we consider the fistula as the cause, or as the effect, it is certain that a bad state of health is often joined with a fistula ani, and the mischief, after the cure of the ulcer, has many times fallen upon other parts, and particularly the lungs, and has brought on asthmas, spittings of blood, and consumptions. For this reason it is a common, and appears to be a reasonable practice, to make an artificial discharge by an issue, as soon as the wound is healed, in order to drain off any of those diseased humours, which at first occasioned the mischief, or were afterwards occasioned by it; and to recommend such a regimen as a consumption requires.

CHAP. 41.

Fluor Albus.

THE fluor albus is a weakness which has been known to incommode females in every year of their lives, from the first to extreme old age; but it is very rarely observed in children, and most usually is first heard of about the time of puberty.

This discharge, though generally white, as the name imports, and thin, yet has sometimes had almost a gelly-like consistence, and not unfrequently a tinge of yellow: in a few women it has been greenish, with an offensive smell. The sharpness of the humour frets the parts, if not duly washed, so as to occasion heat, itching, or soreness, and the urine of course will occasion a little smarting. It is evident from this account, that great attention is necessary to distinguish this disorder from a Venereal infection, wherever there is a possibility of its having been communicated. When a woman has lived entirely free from the fluor albus, or has had it only in a slight degree, and all at once, upon cohabiting with a man, finds a great pain in making water, and the discharge suddenly appear, or greatly increased, with a deep yellow or greenish hue, there will be strong reason to suspect an infection. It unluckily happens, that a woman soon after marriage is particularly subject to this disorder, especially if she be of a weakly make, which has often created great uneasiness, and many disagreeable suspicions: in these circumstances much caution is necessary in passing judgment upon the nature of the discharge. If the colour of it remain white, or at the deepest is only of a faint yellow, and the smarting of the urine little or none, there will be no reason to believe it more than a simple weakness, even though the person should never have experienced any thing of it before.

The most common cause of this malady is frequent miscarriages, or lyings-in. It has made its first appearance, or been increased, in many women during the state of pregnancy; yet I have met with one, who thought herself freer from it at that time. This flux

has in many instances returned every month instead of the menstrual one; or has continued
without ceasing during an obstruction of the
menses, and is not unusual in elderly women
just after their final disappearance. A too profuse menstrual evacuation, and this, will often
harass the same subject, both of them being
perhaps owing to too great weakness. Too
violent exercise, the lifting or carrying of too
great weights, intemperate venery, great dis-
turbances of mind, and a weakly or strumous
habit of body, have been no uncommon
causes. Whatever may have been its origin,
the patient is sure to find it accompanied with
a great pain of the loins, and this is not the
least part of their sufferings. Such a constant
drain must probably in some measure lower
the health and strength, but it is not easy to
point out any other ill consequences. We
meet with many women who have had it
for a great part of their lives, and have not
been hindered by it from bearing healthy
children.

Where a weakness of the whole habit, or a
partial one of the glands which supply this
humour, are judged to be the only causes, the
remedies must be calculated to make the
whole body more robust, or to strengthen the

parts concerned. A powder made of oliba-
num and Seville orange peel, each ten grains,
with five grains of oak bark, taken twice a day,
and washed down with an infusion of Peruvian
bark, has had a good effect; and so has a decoction of oak bark, in the proportion of one
ounce to a quart of water, injected into the
vagina night and morning. These together
with cold bathing have proved the most
powerful helps. But this disorder, though
not dangerous, is often very obstinate from the
length of time it has lasted, or from some constitutional weakness; and will only admit of
being checked, and lessened, but never will be
entirely cured. Besides, in strumous habits it
is not merely a weakness, but a drain by
which part of the noxious humours is carried
off: this creates an additional difficulty of
curing it, and an impropriety of attempting it
merely by strengthening remedies. Where
such have been used in these cases, and have
either stopped or considerably lessened the discharge, the patients have presently complained
of pains of the stomach, and have found a
general illness, by which they were far more
hurt than by the former flux. To such patients injections must not be prescribed; instead of which, together with internal strength-

ening medicines, they should twice a week take some gentle purging waters, or some of the neutral salts dissolved either in water, or in an infusion of Peruvian bark. Bristol water has the reputation of being useful in this complaint, which I have no reason to think it deserves. I have known cases in which saccharum Saturni had been used without effecting a cure; but if it had been ever so successful, the consequences of taking such a dangerous substance would have been far more prejudicial than the distemper.

Excruciating pains of the womb and hips and thighs, which belong to an ulcer or cancer of the womb, together with the sanious and bloody appearance of the gleet, will generally be sufficient to distinguish it from the fluor albus.

CHAP. 42.

Gonorrhœa Mitis.

A GLEET in men resembles the fluor albus both in its nature and cure; so that very little needs here be added to what has been already said under the last article. Such a weakness is far less common in men, than in women; being hardly ever known in them, without being owing to Venereal excesses, or diseases. However, I have been a witness to two or three cases, in which a blow had brought on a copious discoloured flux, exactly resembling that from a Venereal infection, except that it went off spontaneously in a few days.

Injections into the urethra should be used sparingly, if at all, if I am not mistaken in supposing that the free use of them has been the cause of many strictures, as they are called, of the urethra, attended with an extreme difficulty and excessive pain in making water, which too often prove an incurable torment, and end in a fatal suppression of urine, or a mortification. An abstinence from the causes which brought on the gleet, seldom fails to cure it, or to reduce it so far as never to do any material injury to the health. Yet many timid minds suffer more from their apprehensions of the consequences of this complaint, than of any other; and interested people have endeavoured to aggravate those fears, in order to make an advantage of them by the sale of their silly books and insignificant medicines.

CHAP. 43.

Graviditas.

MOST of the complaints incident to breeding women are to be cured only by their delivery. Women readily conceive a little before the time of the menstrual flux. Do they more readily at that time, than at any other?

A healthy woman in the fifth month of pregnancy began to perceive a moisture oozing from the nipples, which continued till two days before her delivery: the breasts were then quite dry for six days, but on the fourth day after the delivery they were filled with milk.

I have been told by two married men, that their wives were free from all Venereal appetite; yet they both of them had been pregnant, and had borne several children.

Pregnancy is very commonly accompanied with sickness and with the heartburn: where these two complaints have been excessive, after a variety of means had been used in vain, the sickness has been cured by rubbing in the anodyne balsam upon the region of the stomach, and the heartburn by repeated doses of elixir of vitriol.

A woman not suspecting her condition, went on bathing frequently for the first months of her being with child, and drinking the sea water so as to be purged two or three times every day; and this was the only time she ever escaped a sickness, which she had suffered in an uncommon degree with all her other children. The juice of oranges and lemons, and plenty of fruit, have also proved remedies for the same sickness.

A violent uterine discharge of blood has continued for six weeks about the sixth month, without occasioning a miscarriage. I knew one, who never ceased to have regular returns of the menstrua during four pregnancies, quite to the time of her delivery.

Consumptive women readily conceive, and during their pregnancy the progress of the consumption seems to be suspended; but as soon as they are delivered, it begins to attack them with redoubled strength; the usual symptoms come on, or increase with great rapidity, and they very soon sink under their distemper.

A difficulty, or total suppression of urine, is sometimes occasioned by the weight of the womb pressing upon the urethra, which can only be relieved by the catheter. After a suppression for three days, upon introducing a catheter, five pints of water came away. Large blisters applied to some pregnant women, who were peculiarly liable to the strangury, have occasioned it in so violent a degree, as to endanger a miscarriage.

CHAP. 44.

Hæmorrhoïdes.

THE veins towards the extremity of the rectum are liable to be surcharged with blood, in consequence of which they sometimes burst, and bleed without any pain, like the veins in the inside of the nostrils; at other times they swell, without bursting, to a considerable size both within and without, and are in great pain even after they have begun to bleed. This discharge of blood is commonly reputed to be wholesome, and the checking of it by forcible means, it is supposed, will occasion head-achs, giddiness, pains of the stomach, and even lay the foundation of a broken state of health, some great mischief being deposited upon the vitals by that blood, which should have found an outlet through the hæmor-rhoïdal vessels. Now, we know very well, that

P

in a perfectly healthy state there is no want of this evacuation, and wherever it happens, it may perhaps more justly be called a symptom, than a remedy of any disease.

In many people the veins of the rectum bleed from as trivial causes as those of the nostrils, and there is no harm in neglecting such an hæmorrhage. There are several diseases of the abdominal viscera, which put some obstruction to the free passage of the blood through them, and this may probably occasion a breach in the lowest part : so we find that in affections of the liver, hæmorrhoïdal bleedings are very common, and possibly may give some little relief at the time, but are not likely to contribute at all to the cure. Bowel disorders too often prove fatal; and if the bleeding of the piles should have been checked by any applications, the mischief may falsely be attributed to the want of that evacuation. I have heard a few persons say, that a head-ach, an asthma, a giddiness, a redness of the face, and a pain of the stomach, had been prevented, or removed, by bleeding piles. There is some difficulty in determining whether they were mistaken, which might easily happen; but certainly the benefits of the piles are by no means so frequent, and so evident, as to make any one either wish for them, or be pleased with having them. There is however no very great use in deciding the question of the wholesomeness of the piles, the bleeding being seldom so excessive as to threaten either present danger, or future mischief. Yet in rare cases I have known so great a flow of blood from them every day for a month together, that it unquestionably weakened the patient. But even in this state of the piles, it is hardly ever found necessary to go beyond the use of half a pint of the decoction of the bark taken at three or four times every day, which perhaps acts less as a styptic, than by obviating the ill effects of such profuse bleedings.

The piles spare neither sex; they have begun so early as at the age of five years; but they very seldom molest children, and may rather be considered as the disorder of adults. Women during the state of pregnancy, and just after the menses have finally left them, are peculiarly subject to the piles: at all other times they are less troubled with them than men.

The piles are habitual in many constitutions, and have continued through life with no great interruption. Both costiveness, and purging will irritate them. They will not only bleed at every stool, but a serous moisture will constantly ooze out spontaneously without any ulcer. The blood does not appear intimately mixed with the excrement, but lying upon it. The pain is greatly increased by going to stool, and will last for some hours after. A heat of urine, a sickness, and pain of the loins, are sometimes, though rarely, complained of together with the piles. Aloes is carefully avoided in this disorder, as a purge which particularly irritates the rectum, and not without some little reason; but it appears to me, that it has not such an effect so generally, and so strongly, as is commonly imagined; and it will therefore often disappoint those who, having a persuasion of the salutary nature of the piles, endeavour in some cases to bring them on by giving an aloëtic purge.

In all hæmorrhoïdal pains and bleedings, the body should for evident reasons be kept in a state rather inclining to laxity, than costiveness; flowers of sulphur in the quantity of ten or fifteen grains have the reputation not only of effecting this in a gentle and proper manner, but of having some further power of soothing the pain and lessening the discharge: however, it is so doubtful whether sulphur have in this disorder any other virtue than that of a laxative, that there might perhaps be safely substituted for it a little lenitive electuary, or a spoonful of castor oil, or half an ounce of tincture of senna mixed with one ounce of oil of sweet almonds, all which I have seen used with an equally good effect.

The pain is sometimes so excessive as to require immediate relief, and this may be procured by means of a cataplasm of bread and milk with a little oil; or, in a less troublesome way, by keeping the parts anointed with a mixture of a dram of the softened extract of opium and two ounces of any simple ointment. No facts have satisfied me, whether opium act in this case as a topical anodyne, or in its usual manner of affecting the whole nervous system when applied to any part of the stomach or intestines. The pain, if occasioned by immoderate distension of the veins, will be lessened, or cease, upon their being emptied either by the point of a lancet, or the application of leeches. I have two or three times been assured by hæmorrhoïdal patients, that a pint of an infusion of box leaves taken night and morning has greatly contributed to their cure; but I have never recommended them, because the helps above mentioned appear sufficient to do every thing that is required, and with as much expedition as the nature of the case will admit.

Chap. 45.

Hernia.

RUPTURES require no other remedy, than a proper bandage, or truss.

Chap. 46.

Hydrocephalus.

THE heads of children sometimes grow enormously large, the sutures give way, and the membranes of the brain are pushed up with the water within, and make a soft tumor rising above the edges of the sutures. This disorder happens to weakly children, and has been growing upon them above a month. They daily become more and more stupid, with a pulse not above seventy-two. They can hardly be got to take any thing for the last week, even out of a spoon, and seem to have no sense, and hardly utter any sound, and have frequent little convulsions.

Upon opening a child who died in this manner, half a pint of water was found in the ventricles. I have no experience of the use of any other means than purging and blistering, and these have not succeeded. The subjects of the hydrocephalus are chiefly children of both sexes, from the first to the eighth year of their lives. Pains of the head, the hands frequently lifted up to the head, sudden exclamations, convulsions, stupidity, deliriousness, a slow pulse, and lastly blindness, usually attend the hydrocephalus, and make it suspected, even without any unnatural enlargement of the head; but still these are not constant and infallible signs of a dropsy in the head. No unusual quantity of water was found in the head of a child, who died after suffering all these complaints. An adult was seized with intolerable pains of the head, sometimes had a voracious appetite, and sometimes none, became delirious, convulsed, stupid, and died : the ventricles of the brain were found so distended with water, that as soon as a puncture was made, the water flew out to a considerable distance.

CHAP. 58.

Lumborum Dolor.

THE loins are the seat of various pains derived from many different causes, such as the gout, rheumatism, a sudden cramp of the muscles lasting two or three days, and making all motion intolerable, gleets, fluor albus, stones and ulcers of the kidneys, ulcers of the womb, pregnancy, and the approach of an abortion. I saw one person, who had complained of a pain in this part for fifty years, but this was only slight, as may readily be imagined. However I attended another, in whom a pain of the loins had been violent above seven years, and motion increased it to such a degree, that during all this time the patient was incapable at best of bearing a carriage, except for a very short time, and frequently could not be moved from one chamber to another without great difficulty; and yet there was no external appearance of harm, nor any such derangement of the animal functions, as to point out the cause; neither was the nature of the complaint to be ascertained from the ef-

U

fect of any medicines, which were tried for its relief. This woman at last recovered. The remedies for this pain must be the same, which are proper for the distemper of which it is a symptom; or such as have been mentioned in chap. 29. under the article of pain in general.

CHAP. 59.

Lumbrici.

BESIDE the round worms, the ascarides *, and the two kinds of flat worms, there are probably many other small animals taken in with our food, capable of living, and breeding in the human intestines.

The symptoms, which have been found joined with worms, and which, upon their being brought away, have ceased, are pains in the head, giddiness, sleepiness, restless sleep, and waking out of it in a fright and with outcries, convulsions, feverishness, thirst, paleness, a bad taste in the mouth, offensive breath, cough, shortness of breath, itching of the nose, pains of the stomach, sickness, loss of appetite, voraciousness, wasting of the flesh, tenesmus, itching

* Concerning the *Ascarides*, see chap. 10.

of the fundament towards night, and lastly skins and slime in the stools.

The tape, or flat worms are the most injurious to health: the round worms and ascarides would sometimes hardly be suspected, if they were not discovered by the itching of the fundament, or did not appear among the fæces. I have seen a tape worm of the length of four ells, which came away at once. Separate joints of it are often voided alive. The round worms will come up alive into the mouth, and I have known them live two or three days after they were come out. In two instances, which have occurred to me, there was ground to suspect that the jointed tape worm had occasioned epileptic fits, madness, and idiotcy.

We have the misfortune to have innumerable remedies for the worms; this being pretty generally a sure sign, that we have not one, upon which we can with certainty depend. Spirit of turpentine, oil, infusions of tobacco, and mercurials, which are such deadly poisons to many small animals out of the body, have been thrown up in clysters without destroying the ascarides; they, and probably the other worms, being so defended by the mucus, in which they lie, that they are secure from the action of any noxious powders, or liquors. Until there-

fore the reputation of a specific for worms be
better established in some of the many medicines which lay claim to it, nothing better can
be done, than giving purging medicines of any
kind which are best borne, and can be repeated
without creating too great a degree of loathing.
Bitters either joined with these, or in the inter-
mediate times, may be useful, not that I have
any reason to believe them hurtful to worms,
but because they will help to restore the disordered stomach and bowels to their natural
strength. A pint of water with as much common salt as could be dissolved in it, has more
than once been of singular use in expelling
worms from the intestines *.

Chap. 60.

Lymphaticæ Glandulæ.

BLISTERING plasters are apt to make the neighbouring lymphatic glands swell, but this swelling has generally soon disappeared. After a
blister the whole arm of one person continued
to be swelled for a long time; probably from
some obstruction of the lymphatic vessels. A
blister applied to the head has in several persons so obstructed the course of the lymph, that

* See *Med. Trans.* vol. i. p. 54.

the whole forehead has been enormously swelled for a day or two. This swelling has gradually descended to the cheeks, and chin, and neck, and then disappeared.

In an old woman, who seemed otherwise healthy, and in particular had no disease of the breast, the lymphatic glands under the arm began to swell, and be obstructed, in consequence of which the whole arm and hand swelled to an enormous sise without pitting, and after a little while she died. Likewise in a young man the face, and head, and breast were greatly swollen without pitting, the veins of the breast were varicous; he had pains in his jaws, was sleepless, short breathed, could hardly bear to lie down, and after a few months died.

Chap. 61.

Mammæ.

It has been known that milk has continued to fill one or both the breasts of a woman for four months, for five, for six, for seven, and even for twelve months after she had weaned her child. In a nurse, who was seized with the small-pox, the milk went away just at the height of the distemper, and returned copiously as soon as that was over.

A woman in her fortieth year began to feel her breasts swell: they, were soon after filled with milk, which ran out for three months: as soon as this stopped, she became pregnant: she had had no child before for six years.

It often happens to lying-in women, and it may happen to any other, that the breast inflames, and comes to suppuration: the adipose membrane seems to be the seat of this inflammation, the glandular part being very little concerned in it; and it is of no more consequence in this part, than such a sore would be in any other part of the body.

A swelling of the breasts with little, or no pain, except a sense of tension, attends pregnancy, and sometimes the regular menstrual discharge, as well as its obstructions, and various other irregularities. The breasts of women are subject also to pain, either with or without a swelling, which often lasts for a long time, and yet is of as little consequence as their swelling, while they continue free from any hard lump. A slight blow on one of the breasts has occasioned a pain, which lasted at least ten years without the appearance of its ever coming to any further mischief. In a great variety of instances pain has come on without any external cause, and has lasted in some above twelve years, and then has gone off spontaneously : great care should be taken, that this pain be not increased by the pressure and tightness of the stays : a gentle opening medicine may now and then be advisable in such a case. It seldom happens that pain does not occasion a general fulness of the breast, but if there be no hardness, which denotes a beginning scirrhus, the swelling and pain have often been considerable without any mischief ensuing.

A serous, or bloody oozing from the nipple, has been the forerunner of a cancer; and it has likewise often appeared, and the nipple has been for many years drawn in, without making any further progress to that dreadful evil. A scirrhus, or hard lump, though ever so small, formed in the breast, may justly cause some apprehension of ill consequences ; for I have never known a cancer come without being preceded by this : nevertheless I have in many instances remarked, that this has been formed without being followed by a cancer; especially if there have been no previous pain, swelling, or discharge from the nipple. For a lump has frequently been felt by accident in the breast, and might perhaps have been there a considerable time before it was discovered, the breast being in every other respect in its natural state. While a small scirrhus in the breast continues quiet, it is best to forbear all external applications, and additional coverings to keep the breast warmer than usual; nor can I recommend any internal medicines: an exact diet seems to answer all reasonable purposes. Nature will sometimes disperse a scirrhous gland in the breast, as I have several times observed, and particularly in one woman, where the tumor seemed to tend to so much malignity, that it was thought advisable to cut it out: some accidental circumstances delayed the operation for some time; and in the mean while the swelling of the breast became less, and softer, and continued to do so till it totally vanished. These however must be acknowledged to be rare cases; but it is by no means unusual for a scirrhous swelling of the breast neither to grow, nor to be painful for many years, especially if it were formed, as happens in a few women, before the age of thirty. The most usual, and the most dangerous time for the coming of a tumor in the breast, is near, or after, the fortieth year of life; yet in a woman of seventy it has occasioned neither pain, nor inconvenience for seven years, and seemed to have no connexion at last with the distemper of which she died. I have noted one man, in whose breast a scirrhous lump had arisen exactly the same with what is so common in the other sex. In another the breast became cancerous, and was successfully cut off.

As soon as a hard tumor in this part begins to be uneasy, and to spread with pricking pains, (in which state it has continued for several years before it has broken) many both external and internal medicines have been recommended to check its progress, and to disperse it. I have not seen much reason to confide in any of the means, which are supposed to have the virtue of resolving such a tumor, after having first soothed it to a state of indolence : though in two or three instances, as I have noted, the extract of hemlock has had the reputation, and perhaps justly, of effecting this. But then it has undeniably failed in so many others, that it is in my judgment not worth any body's while to waste, in making a trial of it, any of that time, which is so precious after the tumor has once begun to make advances towards ulceration. The insignificant pain of cutting it out, while it is small, and the prospect of its healing readily on account of the smallness of the wound, and of the health not being yet much hurt, should determine every one to the operation at this time. If the breast be curable, this, I am persuaded, will be the best cure; and supposing that the mischief is not local, but that the whole body is infected either with an hereditary, or an acquired cancerous taint, I am not aware that the distemper would either more certainly, more rapidly, or more painfully put an end to life, for having made this most promising effort to elude its power.

If the want of resolution in the patient to have the scirrhus taken out, or the delay occasioned by the trial of various specifics, which had promised much, and performed nothing, have suffered the hardness gradually to occupy the whole breast, and to ulcerate, with a great increase of pain in the part, and flying pains over the whole body, and hectic fever, and loss of appetite, of flesh, and of strength, (at which state it may arrive in a few years, or in a few months) what is then to be done? Now even in this state, if the schirri have not spread too far under the arm-pit to be all cut out, the time of the operation is indeed almost over, but not entirely; for in these almost hopeless circumstances I have known it performed with success. It can be no wonder, when done so late, that the operation often fails, and that the wound should either never heal, or that fresh scirrhi should arise after it has been healed ; still there will be some advantages in giving a little respite to the patient, and her attendants, from the offensive-ness of a foul ulcer, by removing at once the putrid mass.

Where the cancer has spread deeply under the arm, and the whole arm is swelled from the obstruction of the lymphatic glands, with loss of appetite, and strength, and shortness of breath, and every sign of inevitable death, all which then remains to be done, is to keep the ulcer with proper dressings, (by washing it with water impregnated with fixed air, or by the application of a carrot poultice in which this air abounds) as clean, and as quiet, as may be; and to sooth the pains, and procure rest with as much opium as is necessary for these purposes. The degree of pain attending a cancer is extremely various; in some it appears to be great, and in others but slight and inconsiderable.

Chap. 62.

Menstrua.

THE regular and natural state of the menstrual flux in women is well known to be intimately connected with their health. They seldom suffer much from any distemper without experiencing some deviations in this particular from the orderly course of nature; and the ir-

regularities of this evacuation, if they continue
long, except in pregnancy, will most commonly
have bad effects upon the general health ; but
these irregularities are perhaps oftener a sign,
than the cause of other distempers.

The proper time of the first appearance of the
menstrua, is from the age of twelve years to fifteen. Some shew of them has been known in
girls of eight, or nine years, and even of five
years ; but I never knew an instance of their
continuing to return regularly, when they began
sooner than the tenth year of life. These very
early appearances have not been attended with
any ill consequences, and required only a little
rest and patience.

When the catamenia begin first to flow at the
proper time, it happens to many young women,
that for the first year or two they will not go on
to observe their exact periods, without either ex-
ceding, or falling short of the just quantity : in
this case, and likewise where they delay to
come on for one or two years beyond the usual
time, it is better not to be too hasty in prescribing
medicines; for as the strength of the body increases, nature will most usually set all such
little anomalies to right, where there is no other
distemper, and in the mean time the constitution will suffer no harm.

The case is very different after women are come to their full growth, and strength; for every function of life will suffer, and often in a violent manner, from great disorders of this evacuation; yet nature has allowed some latitude, so that no inconvenience will arise from the catamenia coming a week sooner or later, staying a day less or more: all which we find by experience to be very consistent with good health.

There are constitutions, in which not only miscarriages, difficult births, and frequent lyings-in; but even terror, uneasiness of mind, and moderate exercise, occasion such a loss of uterine blood, as hath brought on great pains in the head, back, and bowels, and a dangerous weakness. Sometimes without any apparent cause the menses have exceeded the healthy limits, by returning too often, or by continuing to flow too long, or in too great abundance. These hæmorrhages have been so lasting as to have continued for many months together; or so profuse, as by their abundance to have threatened immediate death. But these cases, where pregnancy was not concerned, have been usually more alarming than dangerous: for among the many instances of excessive floodings which I have known, I have remarked only two, who, without being pregnant, have bled till they were exhausted, and died.

The menstrual discharge gradually lessens between the fortieth and fiftieth year; and sometimes misses for two or three periods, and after giving warning in this manner for a year or two, it then totally ceases. This seems to be the most natural way of its going off. But it very commonly happens, that at this time the uterine flux, instead of lessening, returns more frequently, and with more violence; so that, except in cases of pregnancy, the greatest uterine hæmorrhages have been observed at the time when nature is about ceasing to supply them any longer.

Young unmarried women sometimes have their monthly evacuation too often, and in too great quantity, but they are more subject to having it flow too sparingly, or to its not observing the reguar periods, or to its being totally obstructed.

The obstruction of the catamenia has been imputed by the persons themselves to wetting their feet at the time of this flux, to terror, and to frequent venæsections. The injury done by difficult births more frequently occasions floodings, but has sometimes been followed by obstructions, especially if the milk continued to come into the breasts, which it has been known to do for several months after the child had been weaned, or though it had never sucked. Some distemper of the parts concerned, or a male conformation probably occasions irregularities or obstructions in some, especially in those, for such there are, who never experienced this evacuation. But perhaps obstructions are most frequently owing to other antecedent disorders of the health, which by weakening the powers of life, and hindering the due nourishment of the body, reduces it to such an exhausted state, as to afford no supply for this evacuation. If a woman ever so regular in this particular happen to have a long fever, the menstrual discharge is almost always obstructed. So likewise consumptive women in the last stage of their distemper cease to have their courses return merely from their weak and exhausted condition.

The effects which I have noted of suppressed menstruation, where it was not wholly dependent upon other disorders, are a weight and pain of the head, giddiness, a pale, and often bloated appearance of the face, flatulence, sickness, loss of appetite, indigestion, pains and a sense of fulness in the stomach and bowels, a swelling of the belly, which may be mistaken for pregnancy, pains of the breast, sides, back, and knees, swelling of the legs, loss of flesh, sleepiness, flushings, lassitude, fainting, melancholy, and the whole train of hysteric symptoms. The fluor albus has been a substitute for the menses, returning regularly for several months. The catamenia have in more uncommon cases been represented by a periodical bleeding of the nose, or by a vomiting of blood. Barrenness is an usual attendant upon any considerable deficiency of the menses; yet I have known a woman have children, who was not above twice in the year in the way in which she should have been every month.

The menstrua are often regular both as to time and quantity, but attended always with so much pain about the womb, as to occasion greater present misery, than any other irregularity, though with less hurtful consequences. This pain is most usually felt on the first day, and sometimes only for the first six hours, and is then so violent, as to make the persons keep their beds. In two or three instances I have known it not come on till the second day. A strangury has begun to be troublesome only on the last day. Pains of the head, limbs, back, and stomach, and particularly of the breasts, which are usually fuller at this time, together with sickness, and tenesmus, with all kind of hysteric evils, harass some women during the whole time of their menstruation.

The catamenia in the ordinary course of nature cease between the fortieth and fiftieth year. A very few have lost them before the fortieth (and one even before the thirtieth year of life) and yet enjoyed a good state of health afterwards, and have lived long. I have remarked some, who have continued to have them till they were sixty years old. They have become irregular in their time, and quantity, not only a few months, which is their common method, but even for a few years, before they have entirely disappeared; and after ceasing three or four years have been known to return. The animal powers, while the menses are preparing to cease, seem to be greatly oppressed, and less able to keep any constitutional disorder under, or to exert themselves in shaking off any accidental illnesses, which therefore at this time are unusually troublesome, and less disposed to yield to their proper remedies; so that any lurking gout, or madness, or cutaneous diseases, have often taken the advantage of this weak state of the health, and have established a lasting tyranny.

It is probable that the menstrua leave most

women in a kindly manner without exciting, or creating any disorders, which require the assistance of medicine. But some upon the occasion of this great change in the animal œconomy experience a variety of disorders. The most common is that of excessive floodings, attended sometimes with faintings, and convulsions, which though hardly ever immediately fatal, yet are always very alarming, and have been succeeded by dropsical swellings of the legs, of the abdomen, and of the whole body, and by a broken state of health, from which some are with great difficulty, and others never recovered. In the intervals of these discharges the fluor albus often conspires to drain away the strength. Sleepiness, numbnesses, and palsies have followed, and probably have been occasioned by these weakening complaints. Cramps, and wandering pains have been the next most general attendants upon this revolution in the health of women; which may perhaps be the effect of a great loss of blood, where the catamenia have gone off in this manner; for I have observed the same after other immoderate bleedings. Giddiness, and shortness of breath belong also to this train of evils: but no part seems to suffer more, than the stomach and bowels, which are apt to be afflicted at the time of this change with pains, sickness, loss of appetite, heartburn, flatulence, an uneasy sense of fulness, the tenesmus, and piles. Every hysteric symptom has joined itself with these disorders. The legs at this time of life are more peculiarly liable to inflammations, and obstinate ulcers. It is less to be wondered that some constitutions sink under the greatness, or multiplicity of such evils, than that others after struggling three or four years under several of the worst of them, have happily been restored, and their health perfectly established. Perhaps when the menstrua are fully over, after escaping, or surmounting these difficulties, the health of a female becomes firmer than ever, and she bids more fairly for long life, than a man of the same age.

After the menses have disappeared at the natural time, and have seemed for many years to be totally gone, they have in some women returned beyond all expectation. This has happened at the sixtieth, at the seventieth, and even at the eightieth year of life; and consequently after they had ceased for twenty or thirty years. In some of these they have observed their ordinary periods, as they had done in the earlier part of life; but these unseasonable discharges have oftener been irregular in their returns, too abundant in quantity, or joined with the fluor albus. The catamenia have in this manner returned and continued for seven years from no apparent cause, and without any evident injury to the health. This effect however most usually proceeds from some unnatural state of the womb; and if these discharges be accompanied with great pains about the os pubis, the hips, and the loins; and if in their intervals an offensive, discoloured liquor drain away, they may justly be charged to an ulcer of the womb, which usually becomes cancerous, and incurable.

A profuse uterine hæmorrhage may be occasioned by something in the womb, which must be brought away before the bleeding can be restrained. In other cases the patient should be kept quiet and cool; the body must be rather inclining to purging, than costiveness; and liquors should be frequently sipped acidulated with lemon-juice, or acid of vitriol. A dram or two of syrup of poppies will often be of great use in soothing a restlessness or anxious state of mind, which increase the malady. A very able and experienced physician * has proposed to me in consultation the giving of one scruple

* Sir Edward Wilmot.

of flowers of sulphur morning and night to such patients, where he judged it to be as useful, as in an immoderate flow of the piles. The Peruvian bark is seldom omitted among the remedies prescribed in this case; and other styptic substances, as alum, galls, and oak-bark, are often joined with it, as well as given without it. If I were satisfied that experience of the good effects of such medicines had established their reputation, no reasoning, however specious, would make me hesitate to confide in them; but if they be used because of the sense of astringency which they impart to the tongue, it may be questioned whether this quality can afford us a reasonable expectation of their stopping the bleeding in a part, which they cannot reach till after they have been diluted by a great quantity of various liquids: and what degree of effectual stypticity can they then be supposed to possess, when they are not readily able to restrain the bleeding of a small wound made by a leech, though the powder of these substances be immediately applied to the orifice? I am cautious of opening a vein for reasons given in the second volume of the Medical Transactions, Query the fourth. One scruple of alum has been given every day with safety: but I remember to have seen one woman near fifty years old in a bad state of health, whose belly and pudenda were swelled in a remarkable manner, so as almost to close up the vagina, all which was attributed (perhaps without reason) to checking an uterine hæmorrhage by taking daily ten grains of alum. Four grains of saccharum Saturni stopped a profuse bleeding, as I was informed, in four hours; but the violent and lasting colic which I saw occasioned by this preparation of lead, ought to make every one dread its use. Thirty drops of tinctura Saturnina had been taken every day by a woman for a like purpose, whom I afterwards saw labouring under a similar, though less violent, disorder of the bowels. Steel waters have in several instances increased the hæmorrhage. Chamomile flowers have done the same: and so likewise has lying down; contrarily to what I should have supposed.

The opposite disorder to flooding, namely, where the catamenia are too sparing, or totally obstructed, may be occasioned, as was before observed, by a variety of other complaints, the remedies of which will be the likeliest means of rectifying all the ailments dependent upon them. But where there appears no ill health, except what is the effect, rather than the cause of the partial or total obstruction, there stimulating, bitter, aloëtic, and chalybeate medicines are what physicians from general experience seem to have rested in; various forms of which are to be found in all pharmacopœïas. The black hellebore root claims some specific virtue as an emmenagogue, of which in my practice I have never met with any decisive proof. Chamomile flowers undoubtedly possess it with relation to particular women; for I have known more than one, in whom they constantly brought on some degree of an uterine hæmorrhage, at whatever time of the month they were taken. Warm bathing, putting the feet in warm water, and sitting over its vapor for half an hour every day, have been used successfully. Electrifying, when employed for other purposes, has frequently brought on the menses before their time. But there are too many cases in which all these means have been found ineffectual.

The pains, which several women experience during some part of the menstrual flux, are safely mitigated with opium; and such persons should always have in readiness half a grain or a grain of opium, to be taken as soon as the pain comes on, and to be repeated once or twice if the pain require, at the distance of half an hour. This has been very frequently given without checking, or in any manner deranging this evacuation. To those, whose stomach will not bear opium, it has been given as safely in a clyster. The tincture of opium has not appeared to be without some effect, when only rubbed in by a warm hand over the abdomen. Warm bathing, sitting over the steam of warm water a few mornings before the expected return of the catamenia, Bath waters both externally and internally, have all been employed against this complaint, and with advantage.

At the time of life, when it is according to the course of nature that the menstrual flux should entirely cease, if it go off gradually and without any troublesome symptoms, which it most frequently does, no medicines will be wanted; nature herself being fully sufficient to bring about this revolution without any tumult or commotion. However, some attention may be useful in keeping the body from any tendency to costiveness, by taking occasionally a little lenitive electuary, or some purging water. If the menses leave a woman very abruptly, and either from this cause, or from any other, there should come on at this time vertigos, sleepiness, numbnesses, or pains of the head with a sense of fulness, the taking away of six ounces of blood by cupping once a month, as long as these complaints remained, has been experienced with success. Whatever other disorders may chance to shew themselves, they must be treated with their usual remedies. In constitutions, which have been subject to cutaneous diseases, or which may be judged to be in danger from palsies, or some hereditary cancerous taint, an issue may be advisable; which in other cases, as far as I have observed, may very safely be omitted.

A return of the menstrual flux to old women, after having left them for some years, may either be excessive, or it may be a symptom of an ulcered, or cancerous womb; and then the proper remedies for these ails must be employed: but if it continue to make its visits in a regular manner, as it has happened to some women, and the health appear in no respect to suffer, such persons will stand in need of no assistance from physicians.

CHAP. 63.

Morbilli.

I PURPOSE first to give a history of the measles in a single patient, who had a regular

and middling sort, and in whom, on account
of the fairness of the skin, it was easy to observe
with preciseness the appearance, and disappearance of the eruption: after which I will relate
the varieties, which I have noted in a considerable number of other patients.

On the first day

The symptoms were very slight shiverings, a
failure of appetite, some degree of sickness, a
quickness of pulse, a dry cough, no sneezing,
no tears, nor redness of the eye-lids, a very little
thirst, and pains in the limbs.

2d. The night was quiet without any great
complaint, the appetite still fails, and the cough,
and pulse are as before.

3d. This day all is much the same as yesterday.

4th. A faint eruption is to be seen by attentive
looking upon the face: red spots are much
more visible about the throat. The fever, restlessness, and want of appetite, are increased.
The cough is rather less. The eyes are less
impatient of light. There is no vomiting. The
face burns, and is unusually flushed.

5th. Faintly red spots are sprinkled over the
chin, and (at a greater distance from one another) over the rest of the face. The spots are
of an irregular figure, and are much redder

about the throat and breast. The fever and cough remain. There is yet no appearance of the eruption on the hands and arms.

6th. The spots of the face rise a little above the skin so as to afford a perceivable roughness to the touch, and are visibly formed of many minute heads much less than a millet seed. On this day the eruption begins to appear on the arms. The fever, and restlessness, and impatience are considerably increased. The cough is very troublesome, but without any difficulty of breathing. The eyes are weak, the eye-lids are swelled. There is a total loathing of all food. Towards evening the symptoms grow worse, and with some oppression of the breath. The spots in the face are of a lively red. Yesterday the menses came on before their regular time, and lasted only twenty-four hours.

7th. Bleeding yesterday gave some relief. The night was a little quieter; but the fever and anxiety are very little abated. The eruption in the face is paler. The skin begins to itch in a troublesome manner.

8th. The symptoms are much abated, and the appetite begins to return. The eruption is more faint. The languor and fever are now and then much complained of.

9th. The night was tolerably quiet, and the

patient is now a little revived; but still there are intervals of fever, and uneasiness, and lowness, which are much relieved by a repetition of bleeding.

10th. The night was very good. The eruption has totally disappeared, and hardly any fever remains.

11th. Some cough still remains.

12th. The sleep and appetite are returned, but the cough still remains; and so it continued to do for three or four days more: bleeding much weakened it, and in a few days more it went entirely away.

I shall now proceed to relate some diversities in the symptoms, which have attended the several stages of the measles, collected from a considerable number of patients.

Some have had weak and watery eyes one or two days before the eruption, and sometimes the same sharp humour has irritated the nostrils, and occasioned sneezing. The cough most usually has come on two or three days before the eruption; but it has been known to precede the measles seven or eight days, and it generally did so in the year 1753, when they were remarkably epidemical. Pains of the throat and head and back have not been unusual in this preparatory stage. One person in particular

had a most excruciating pain in the back, which
continued a day or two after the eruption.
Sickness and vomiting as well as want of appetite,
have come on at the beginning, and lasted till
the middle, or decline of the distemper. Some
have been so fortunate as to have the measles
appear after suffering so very little from fever
or any of the preparatory symptoms, that they
could hardly say they had been ill. The longer
the preparatory symptoms continued, and the
worse they were, so much the less mild has the
distemper proved.

The first day of the eruption.

In one or two patients I have seen the eruption appear upon the arms on the first day, a
few hours after its having been observed on the
face and neck. But it so seldom happens that
the arms and hands shew any mark of the distemper before the second day of its being visible
on the face, that possibly in those instances the
eruption on the face might have been earlier
than it was taken notice of. In one patient no
cough, nor sneezing was complained of till the
day of the eruption. The appearance of this
distemper does not at all mitigate the symptoms,
as it does in the small-pox. One patient was
seized with a spitting on this day, which conti-

nued to tease him for forty-eight hours without suffering him to rest at all by day, or to sleep by night; the cough in the mean time almost ceased, and all the other symptoms were as mild, as in a favourable sort of the measles.

2d. I have scarcely ever observed the eruption on the hands and arms fail of being perceived in the course of this day; and where it has been supposed to have been deferred a day longer, it is most probable that there was an error in dating the beginning of the eruption. Once or twice the distemper has been observed never to have reached the arms, which throughout the whole of it shewed none of the usual spots. On this day the measles appear in full vigour upon the face, but without any relief of the symptoms, which are often rather aggravated, and a diarrhœa has been joined to them, but without any danger. The nose has bled about this time, and the eye-lids have been so swelled, that for twenty-four hours they could not be opened.

3d. Now the eruption usually appears very lively on the other parts, but is a little deadened upon the face; yet in several the marks on the face have been at this time of as bright a red as ever. In others I have observed them to disappear entirely on this day, and all the other symptoms likewise to retreat. However, the cough and fever most commonly continue the same; some patients have thought them a little better, others a little worse. Where the eyes have been very watery, and the eyelids red, they have still remained so to this time; and I have noted a very troublesome and constant sneezing, which first came on upon this day. A child five years old became comatose the third day of the eruption, and died the next.

4th. The spots in most patients become of a much paler colour in the face, and begin to grow fainter in the breast and arms of some; in others the arms are of as high a colour as ever: yet in more persons than one, I have observed no diminution of the colour even in the face on this day. Those, who have shewn the least remains of the eruption at this time (and some have shewn hardly any) have appeared the best; and in those, where it was still in undiminished vigour, the cough and fever have been the worst. The cough in several is very sensibly abated on this day; others find both cough and fever as bad as ever. The eyes seldom continue to water any longer, except where they have been so hurt by this illness, as to continue weak for a long time after. The sneezing has lasted till this time: but this has very rarely happened. The face now begins to be branny and itch, which itching is propagated over the whole body, so as to be the chief, or only complaint. The catamenia have appeared on this day before their regular time.

5th. The marks are very pale both in the face and arms, though perceivable in some; in others they are quite gone, the appetite returns, and the patients seem well. Those patients have been the worst, in whom most of the eruption was still remaining. The cough in some is much better, in others it is quite gone; but several are teased with it a long time after the distemper is ended. The menses have made their appearance on this day, out of their regular course.

6th. The vestiges of the eruption have been still visible on the arms, and even in the faces of a few patients, with a considerable degree of cough, sneezing, hoarseness, and fever; and I have once or twice seen some marks of the measles so late as on the tenth day of the eruption; but on the sixth day most patients are tolerably well recovered, except in those unfortunate cases, in which the fever, instead of abating, begins at this time to increase, and continues to do so, until it have destroyed the patient. In others, who escape this immediate danger, the lungs are sometimes so injured by this distemper, that a lasting cough succeeds; and sometimes a pulmonary consumption. Weak eyes, inflamed eye-lids, glandular tumors, and many other scrofulous appearances have followed the measles; whether they were formed by them, or, the seeds being before in the constitution, were only excited by this distemper; or possibly the appearance of scrofulous symptoms was wholly owing to other causes, and would have come on at this time though there had been no measles.

Bleeding may be used at any time of the measles, and is always beneficial where the symptoms are very distressing, particularly if there is an oppression of the breath, to which every stage of this distemper is liable. Bleeding, together with such medicines as the occasional symptoms would require in any other fever, is the whole of the medical care requisite in the measles. The flowing of the menses ought to be no objection to the opening a vein, if the cough and shortness of breath make it otherwise advisable. I never saw any bad consequences from bleeding a woman in

Y

these circumstances; but the greatest danger might attend the omitting to do it in a violent cough, or oppression of the breath.

The measles are far less dangerous to pregnant women, than the small-pox. I have attended several, who were greatly harassed by the violence of all the usual symptoms in this illness, but I never knew it make one woman miscarry, or be in more danger on account of the pregnancy.

Is not this distemper worse in proportion to the quantity of eruption, as in the small-pox?

The preparatory symptoms of the measles have appeared thirteen days after the infection had probably been received. In two others there was the greatest reason to judge, that they began to come on fourteen days after the time of infection. In four others the infection seemed not to have lain dormant above ten days.

An infant sucked a nurse till the measles appeared upon her, and then was taken away, and escaped catching the distemper: is it therefore, like the small-pox, not infectious in its first stage? or did the incapacity of this child's receiving the measles at that time arise from some other cause?

Chap. 81.

Singultus.

A HICCUP is the companion both of chronical and acute distempers. It has been the fore-
runner of epilepsies, and has attended palsies,
and seldom fails to be one of the symptoms of
diseased livers, and sometimes will belong to
simple obstructions of the gall-ducts. Various
other diseases of the stomach, and bowels, have
this for one of the symptoms; whether they
arise from ruptures, scirrhi, and ulcers, or from
mischief done by the violent operation of drastic
antimonial, or corrosive mercurial medicines.
All these have been the causes of hiccups,
which have lasted for months, and for years;
some almost constant, and others with intervals
of various lengths. One or two patients have
been harassed with them for several months
without any other sign of ill health.

A hiccup is a symptom of a dangerous nature in acute distempers: it has begun on the
first day of a fever, and lasted for the whole
seven days, that the patient lived, without yield-
ing to any of the known helps. In other less

violent, though at last mortal, fevers it has admitted of no relief for twenty days. The cure
of it must either depend on the cure of the
primary distemper; or it must be treated with
antispasmodics, such as moderate doses of opium, or a spoonful of the musk julep frequently
administered.

CHAP. 82.

Sitis.

AN unquenchable thirst, and, what is often
joined with it, a dropsy, or diabetes, are not so
much distempers themselves, as attendants upon
great disorders of the abdominal bowels; which
most commonly admit of no relief, but end in
death. However, the primary malady, though
fatal at last, will in some cases be two or three
years undermining the health, before the patient sinks under it; during all which time he
is harassed with this most distressing ail, which
is usually accompanied with a feverishness, and
loss of appetite, and strength, shortness of
breath, and other signs of a ruined constitution.

Formidable as this sympton is, yet it has not
always been fatal; the original distemper in a
few instances having admitted, and happily
met with a cure. The thirst has been increased

by indulging the desire of drinking; and has been relieved by the use of a little nitre. But unless the principal disease can be put into a successful method of cure, it is plain, that this among other symptoms dependent upon it, though it may be checked, yet is not likely to be entirely subdued.

CHAP. 83.

Spasmus.

INVOLUNTARY agitations, and cramps or involuntary contractions, in those muscles which should obey the will, if much increased, are called convulsions. Every external muscle of the body is liable to spasms, as our senses inform us, and probably all the internal muscles likewise. These preternatural contractions of the muscles have sometimes burst a small blood vessel, and the extravasated blood running under the skin has discoloured it black and blue and yellow, as it appears when bruised.

Cramps and involuntary agitations are familiar to gouty and hysteric patients, and often fore-run and attend palsies, and are the principal symptoms of epilepsies and St. Vitus's dance. The causes of them are either in the nerves only of the part affected, or in the brain and spinal marrow. That species of cramp, called chorda penis, is usually occasioned by the acrimony of the Venereal virus affecting those particular nerves; but it may be brought on by other similar local mischief, for I have twice known it without any Venereal infection. A perpetual agitation of the left leg and arm arose from a purulent mass, into which the right side of the brain was changed, its natural texture being obliterated. Instances of a like nature with these perpetually occur, whether the irritation of the part, or the preternatural state of the brain and spinal marrow, be owing to any disease, or to some external violence.

On the sixth day after the extirpation of a scirrhous testicle, the patient began to complain of a difficulty of swallowing, or rather of a sudden sense of suffocation; and in two days the jaw became immoveably locked, and the patient soon died. I observed the same happen in an hysteric woman without any sore or wound. She died about the tenth day; opium and warm bathing proving ineffectual.

After a dangerous fever the sleep of a man was sometimes broken by excessive cramps. Two or three days previous to such a bad night, there used to appear about the middle of the tibia a small soft tumor, hardly bigger than a pea; and by this never-failing sign the approach of the cramp was certainly known.

In the fevers of children the face is sometimes drawn to one shoulder. I have often seen this, but never knew it continue long after the fever was cured. This happens both in continual, and in intermittent fevers. A similar circumrotation of the face, sometimes to the right, sometimes to the left shoulder, has continued for a long time in several elderly women who had no other complaint; but in them this involuntary motion has been so little violent, as to be overpowered by a very small force, and therefore has ceased while the head rested upon a pillow.

Fevers in the West Indies, as we are told, by some disturbance of the brain, give occasion to those very formidable cramps called emprosthotonus, and opisthotonus: some less derangement has been left by fevers in England, in consequence of which cramps of the legs have returned every night in a most tormenting manner. But the change made in the state of the nerves by a fever has not always in this respect been for the worse; for the only time that one person was free from spasmodic agitations, was during a fever.

Sleep favours the access of cramps, as it does

of all other nervous complaints; and therefore they are chiefly complained of in the night: they attack some just as they are sinking into sleep, and others just as they are waking at the usual time, or forcibly awake them in what would else have been the middle of their sleep. Acids have sometimes brought them on.

Slight cramps are cured by altering the position of the limb. Æther has been rubbed into the calves of the legs at bed-time with success. Habitual cramps have yielded to five drops of tinctura thebaïca mixed with forty drops of tinctura asæfœtidæ taken every night. A fit of the gout has been judged to suspend the power of cramps; but I am much more strongly convinced, that the gout is apt to breed and foster them. A course of warm bathing effectually cured an obstinate cramp, which had for some months kept the body crooked, and one hand immoveably clenched, so that the nails had grown into the palm, and made sores. The waters of Bath have been useful, as it is probable, more on account of their warmth, than of any other qualities. The cold bath has been tried without any benefit.

Chap. 84.

Sputa cruenta.

A CONSIDERABLE spitting of blood, proceeding not from the stomach with the action of vomiting, nor trickling down from the back of the nostrils, but coming from the lungs, is a very just ground of alarm to the patient. This is very seldom seen in children; many having kept free from this, as well as from the other symptoms of a pulmonary consumption, during their childhood, though they were born of consumptive parents, and died of that disease before they were twenty. This complaint has made its first appearance at all times of life from puberty to old age.

The danger belonging to it will be greater in proportion to the greater number and degree of the other consumptive symptoms, with which it is accompanied, and to the tenderness of the age at which it comes on. A spitting of blood seems sometimes to be the whole complaint, so that not even a cough shall be joined with it, but the blood will be brought up with as little effort as the easiest phlegm: it does indeed most commonly denote an unsound state of the lungs; but from many facts it seems reasonable to infer the possibility of a slight hæmorrhage from the vessels of the lungs, or trachea, while the lungs are otherwise in a healthy state, and consequently with as little danger, as from the hæmorrhoïdal vessels, or those of the nose, especially if it happen after the meridian of life. I have seen a man in good health at seventy, who for fifty years had never been free from spitting of blood above two years together. In others I have known it return every now and then for as long time. In a peripneumony a bloody mucus will be brought up as the patient recovers, and no cough, nor sign of any injury remain. A peripneumony, in which bloody phlegm had been spit up for two or three days, gradually abated, and the patient seemed to be recovered; but the cough soon came on again, and in a month's time there was a great wasting of the flesh, and a difficulty of breathing, with many signs of approaching death : After going into the country, and riding, the patient lost his cough and shortness of breathing, and lived healthy for many years. A very considerable wound may be made in the lungs of a healthy man, as I have known, by a bullet, without either death, or a consumption following. The loose texture of the lungs, and their great number of large blood vessels, together with their constant motion, and the impossibility of any topical application, might make one fear, that a large hæmorrhage from them could never be stoppèd, and must prove fatal; yet I have known such a breach entirely cured *, as was probable, from there being no return of spitting blood for near forty years; and I do not remember, as common as this complaint is, to have seen more than one, who was evidently exhausted by large and repeated returns of it, and might truly be said to have bled to death. A man has survived at least for two years the loss of a pint of blood from the lungs every day for a month. Not only the common motion of the lungs is borne without much increasing their hæmorrhage, but a perpetual sickness and vomiting during a voyage of six weeks did not apparently make a spitting of blood more profuse.

These facts may afford some hope in accidents of this kind; which however most frequently end in a quick consumption, or leave a lasting cough, growing worse every winter, and making the breathing more laborious.

* In the second volume of Transactions of a Society for the Improvement of Medical and Chirurgical Knowledge, is given an account of a dissection, where a wound of the lungs had been perfectly healed. E.

Among the notes which I have taken of these cases, I do not find that I have reason to recommend any new remedy, or that I have made any practical remarks upon those which are in common use. The necessity of keeping quiet, and cool, is evident, and therefore of avoiding all strong liquors, high sauces, hot rooms, costiveness, loud speaking, and exertions of all kinds. Two or three large spoonfuls of tincture of roses may be frequently taken with advantage; and there will sometimes in these cases be occasion for a gentle opiate. If I give so much to the established practice as to allow of one or two small bleedings, where the spitting of blood has not already occasioned too great a loss, I must think a caution necessary against large and repeated bleedings, which would probably conspire with the distemper to exhaust the patient.

Chap. 85.

Steatomata.

Two children, one four, the other eight years old, had tumors all over them, some of the size of small nuts, others as large as nutmegs. I judged them to be of a steatomatous kind. One of these children had a voracious appetite:

they were both very weakly, and soon pined away, and died.

Softish subcutaneous tumors, between the size of a pea and that of a small nut, without any pain, have been very numerous in the arms only ; and in another they were chiefly seated about the ancles, elbows, and knees, and were suspected to be Venereal. In a third, similar tumors continued six years in the arms, and then spontaneously retreated. They have lasted so long as ten years.

The large steatomatous swellings, or wens, are safely cut out, and they seem to admit no other cure.

CHAP. 86.

Stranguria.

THE strangury, or a frequent and most urgent desire to make water, with excessive pain in the attempt, is sometimes an attendant upon pregnancy, and usually accompanies diseases of the womb, of the prostate gland, and of the bladder, hard fæces obstructing the rectum, and injuries of the urethra from fresh, or frequent, or ill-cured gonorrhœas.

It has been caused by some sorts of food, and

some medicines, as pepper, particularly long-
pepper, mustard-seed, horse-radish, and other
acrid vegetables, and rough cyder. This pain
has come on from taking six drams of diuretic
salts, and very certainly follows the use of spirit
of turpentine, one dram of which is on this
account a greater dose than can generally be
borne. Cantharides are well known to possess
the same power beyond all other substances,
even applied externally, as well as when taken
into the stomach. It is one among the many
instances of our imperfect knowledge of the
animal œconomy, that we can by no means
understand how the cantharides should pass so
quietly without hurting the various passages,
and some of them of exquisite fineness, through
which they are carried to the bladder, and yet
irritate this part in that extraordinary manner,
which is too often experienced from the application of blisters. The difficulty of accounting for this is increased by our finding, that one
blister has sometimes occasioned this irritation,
though afterwards in the same person, and the
same illness, five blisters applied at once have
had no such effect: and what is called a perpetual blister, after it has been kept open seven
years without doing the least hurt to the blad-

der, has all at once, without any apparent reason, affected it so strongly, as to make it im-
possible to continue the blister any longer.

There are persons, who from some unknown
peculiarity in their constitution, have such a
disposition to the strangury, that after the application of a blister this complaint has continued upon them for several months: others,
without any of the known causes, have frequently had returns of it throughout their
whole lives from their infancy, particularly in
every illness, whatever it were, though no blister
had been applied. It is a disorder familiär to
elderly persons, both men and women; and it
has been suspected, that a tendency to this evil
has been created by a gouty habit.

No medicines taken into the stomach have
appeared to do much good in the strangury.
Oil, and gum arabic, may perhaps do a little;
but I have reason to believe, that camphor, like
other substances of the same class, will create a
dysury, rather than prove its cure. The uva
ursi is at best a doubtful remedy, and yet it is
capable of doing something to the parts concerned in secreting and containing the urine,
for in one patient it was frequently tried, and it
always changed the urine to a green colour.
Bougies have afforded great ease in difficulties

2 E

of urine from Venereal injuries of the urethra, but they have seldom effected a complete and lasting cure. Injections of oil into the urethra, sitting over the steam of warm water, warm fomentations of the perinæum, and about the os pubis, have often procured a truce with these pains; but an opiate clyster made of a quarter of a pint of water, and from twenty to a hundred or more drops of tinctura opii, has most readily cured the strangury arising from a blister, and has been the most certain and expeditious temporary relief in those cases, which admitted nothing further.

Chap. 87.

Struma.

That habit of body is called strumous, or scrofulous, or the evil, in which the lymphatic glands are swelled with little or no pain. This happens most commonly in the neck, and armpits, more rarely in the groin. Those of the mesentery are found liable to the same disorder, and probably all the other internal lymphatic glands. Together with these appearances, the end of the nose, and both the lips are apt to swell, and the eye-lids are often inflamed, and ulcered. These ails have sometimes followed, or been joined with cutaneous eruptions, and purulent discharges from the ears. Some constitutions experience frequent returns of an inflammation of the tonsils, which lasts a few days, not without fever: in others there is an enlargement of them, which sometimes continues for a long time with considerable uneasiness to the patient, and some difficulty of swallowing.

Infants and children are particularly subject to strumous disorders, and more especially the weakly with very fair skins. After the age of puberty the tumors of the glands, and the inflammation of the eye-lids, usually begin to abate, and in adults often disappear entirely; but in some persons, upon their retreat from the outward parts of the body, they seem to fall upon the lungs, whence arise incurable consumptions. But children are not the only sufferers by this malady; for I have noted eight or ten healthy persons, in whom the lymphatic glands began first to be enlarged after the age of thirty, and the swelling in some of them did not shew itself till near their sixtieth year. The origin of this mischief in these adults was probably to be found in the unwholesomeness of their diet, or situation. The use of a very hard water was suspected to have made one of them scrofulous; for he began to be so after using it constantly for a few years, and continued so as long as he used it, but upon leaving it off, all the scrofulous appearances left him. It is most probably owing to some bad quality of the water, that swellings of the throat are endemial in some parts of England, and notoriously among the inhabitants of the Alps; though I by no means think it owing to the use of snow-water, to which it has been attributed: for I believe on account of its great purity this would be one of the best remedies they could employ *.

Beside these swelled glands which make one species of the evil, there is another, which is called the joint evil, which has begun in the hands, or elbows, or feet, with a small tumor situated so deep, that the bones are often af-

---

* The inhabitants of Rheims had been so afflicted with strumous diseases, that they maintained an hospital for the sole purpose of curing such patients. They then made use of no other water than what they had from wells. After a machine was constructed, which brought the water from a neighbouring river, and distributed it into all quarters of the city, it was observed that scrofulous disorders were become less common: in the space of thirty years the number of these patients was reduced to one half of what it had usually been; and it continued to decrease so fast, as to give occasion for thinking, that the greater part of the revenues of the hospital might be applied to other purposes.—*Soc. Royale de Médecine,* vol. ii. *Hist.* p. 230.

fected. These have continued two or three years, before they have come to ulcers, which have been of such a malignant nature, as at length to make the hands or feet almost useless, or to make the fingers and toes fall off. Are the diseases of the head of the thigh-bone, and its socket, and also what is called the white-swelling of the knee, to be referred to this class? This seems not unlikely, as they have been found joined in the same person with the usual marks of an inveterate scrofula.

Some strumous appearances have shewn themselves not long after the measles and small-pox, and this has created a suspicion, that this alteration of the health was to be attributed to some reliques of those diseases; but this has happened too seldom within my observation to give any just grounds for such an opinion; which perhaps has been entertained the more readily, because the patients, or their friends, were unwilling to think the scrofulous complaints hereditary, or constitutional.

The scrofula, and lues Venerea, when they meet, seem greatly to exalt the malignity of each other.

The swellings of the lymphatic glands in the neck, and arm-pits, have continued above twenty years without any other variation, than

being a little enlarged upon catching cold :
but this is extraordinary, and happens but seldom : they more usually either lessen by degrees, and vanish in not many months, or in a
very few years ; or else inflame, and suppurate.
The larger break into smaller parts with a slight
degree of itching in the skin previously to their
going away ; and the smaller first grow softer,
and so gradually sink down, and are reduced
to their natural size ; instances of all which are
very common. When, instead of dispersing,
these tumors inflame and grow red, they are a
long time in coming to a sore, in which state
they are slowly dissolved into an imperfect pus,
and afterwards heal. These sores have never
within my observation shewn a disposition to
turn cancerous in children, and only in two or
three adults.

I never saw any occasion for using poultices,
plasters, or warm covering to strumous swellings. They cannot be wanted to mitigate the
pain, because it is so inconsiderable ; and if it
be meant to disperse them by plasters, it may be
doubted whether any have a power of this
kind ; but if the application be intended to
make them suppurate, it is doing the thing,
which too much pains can never be taken to
prevent ; for they cannot terminate in a worse

manner. If this event cannot be hindered, and the glands spontaneously tend to become ulcerous, they should be suffered to break of themselves without the help of a knife or a caustic; and the mildest defensative plaster is all the further care which they require. The scrofulous inflammations of the eye-lids, and eyes, sometimes make bleeding necessary; and they have been much more benefited by leeches, than by taking away blood in any other manner: two or three may be put to each temple once or twice a week for a considerable time. Many external applications to the eyes are recommended, all which have been often found of very little service, except soft cataplasms put between two pieces of fine linen, and so applied to the eyes, and touching the edges of the sore eye-lids every night with some softened animal fat, which will hinder their being glued together in the night; for the force used to open them in a morning keeps them constantly raw and sore.

Mercurial medicines have been judged to hurt, rather than to help scrofulous patients; and perhaps strumous distempers have been aggravated by the accession of a Venereal infection chiefly on account of the preparations of mercury which these require. Sea water internally and externally, extract of hemlock, bark infused in purging water, or taken in substance at night, while purging waters, or salts, are used in the morning, burnt spunge, sal sodæ, issues, and perpetual blisters, are the principal means which have been recommended as alteratives of a strumous habit; all which, as experience has taught, may be employed with safety; but the reputation of their efficacy is far from being fully established. Where the patient has not perseverance enough to continue the use of any of these for a proper length of time, he may do himself some, and I believe considerable service, by a temperate course of life, and by drinking no other water than such a pure one as that of Malvern.

CHAP. 88.

Tenesmus.

A CONSTANT needing, or wanting to go to stool, though little or no fæces could be voided, has been owing to the following causes: hard fæces, which had loaded the rectum, and which could not be expelled without assistance; a scirrhus of the womb, of the rectum, or of the prostate gland; a stone in the bladder; a strangury, particularly one brought on by cantharides; and a weakness of the sphincter ani left by an apoplexy, or a difficult labour. It is usually troublesome for a little while after a dysentery; and has accompanied the colica Saturnina, and a prolapsus of the inner coat of the intestine.

A tenesmus is usually increased by standing or walking, and relieved by sitting. When it is merely owing to acrimony, an opiate clyster will be the best remedy. In other cases, the relief of this uneasy sensation must depend upon the cure of the original disease, of which it is a symptom.

Chap. 89.
Testiculus.

Besides tumors of the testicles from external, or Venereal injuries, they have been found joined with an intermittent fever, coming on and going off with every fit, and finally ceasing upon the cure of the intermittent: this has happened more than once. A common cold has had a similar effect upon several persons. A scirrhous prostate gland has made the testicles swell; which also is no very uncommon consequence of stones, and other affections of the kidneys. Without any manifest cause a swelling has begun in one of the testicles, and after continuing a few months has spontaneously subsided. A tumor of them has at other times slowly increased for many years, and at last made the whole testicle scirrhous, which has been twenty years before it became cancerous and fatal. A fistulous sore has formed in such a testicle, and has long harassed the patient.

Purges, except very gentle ones, have been at least useless. Poultices are necessary when the pain is considerable. Whether there be pain, or swelling, a bag-truss is of indispensable use to suspend the scrotum. There is no cure for a scirrhous testicle, but castration; and this may be safely performed, if the spermatic chord be in tolerable order; but where this too is diseased, the case admits of no cure. The hydrocele is inconvenient, but void of danger; and may be sufficiently relieved, without pain or hazard, by tapping, as often as there is occasion. An operation is sometimes performed in the hydrocele, which makes a lasting cure.

CHAP. 90.

Torpor.

A NUMBNESS, or sense of tingling in a limb, which is commonly called its being asleep, has been experienced in every part of the body, but chiefly in the limbs, and particularly the extremities. It is a half loss of the sense of feeling, and is extremely common, though a total loss of it be so rare even in the most hopeless palsies.

A numbnesss, like a cramp, has been either a slight complaint brought on by an inconvenient posture, or other trivial causes, unattended with any ill consequences, and presently removed; or else it has arisen from that preternatural state of the nerves, which is inconsistent with tolerable health, or, it may be, with life, and has been the fore-runner of convulsions, palsies, and apoplexies. The old seem most subject to it, and both sexes equally; in youth females have oftener been sufferers than males. Where a torpid state of any part has not been constant, it has been found to come on chiefly in the night, owing partly to a long continuance of the same posture, and partly to sleep, which favours the access of all disorders in which the nerves are more immediately concerned.

Numbnesses are familiar to broken constitutions, and such as have been derived from paralytic parents. They have been the fore-runners, the attendants, and followers of palsies, and apoplexies, and are commonly joined with other symptoms of these maladies. This very frequently makes one of the numerous complaints, which are heard of among hypochondriac and hysteric patients, and has continued in them and others not only for many months, but often for many years, and then has gone off without having done any mischief to the health. The whole left side has been benumbed for five and twenty years.

The true nature and tendency of a numbness may be best known by its attendant circumstances; for if it be associated with other paralytic symptoms, and affect a considerable part of the body, especially in persons derived from paralytic parents, no doubt can be made of its betokening mischief, and the proper preventives of palsies should be employed. But if a torpor should affect only a small part, as one or two fingers, or toes, and be united with no other symptoms, or only such as are common in hypochondriac disorders, the less notice the patient takes of it, the happier he will be. But if there should be reasons for endeavouring to cure this more innocent species of the complaint, blisters, and warm bathing have been found the most serviceable means; cold bathing, and bleeding, have been found prejudicial; the gout has been useless; and as for electricity, its virtues have not yet been sufficiently ascertained.

Chap. 91.

Tremor.

A TREMBLING of the hands, or a shaking of the head, may be judged to have some alliance with paralytic, and apoplectic maladies; yet it has been found by experience, that such a tremor has often continued for a great part of a person's life, without any appearance of further mischief; and therefore, if it have a tendency to palsies, it is a very remote one, and the inconvenience is far more considerable than the danger. Hypochondriac persons are troubled with frequent fits of it; hard drinkers have it continually; and some degrees of it usually attend old age.

This, like other affections of the nerves, is greatest in a morning, and is aggravated by any disturbance of mind. Coffee and tea make the hands of some persons shake; and yet I have known strong coffee drunk every day for forty years by one, who was remarkable for the steadiness of his hands even in extreme old age. There are many others, who know no such ill effect from these liquors; and indeed, if it were general, few Chinese, and Turks, would escape it; but their history does not acquaint us, that these people are more subject to tremors, than those of other nations.

If any medicines are wanted, they must be such as are found serviceable in paralytic and hypochondriac complaints.

Chap. 92.

Tussis.

A COUGH seems to have been sometimes occasioned either by an acrimonious, or a too copious defluxion on the trachea, without any material, or permanent injury of the lungs; or merely by disorders of the stomach and bowels, as hath appeared upon dissections, examples of which are often seen in children with worms, and swelled mesenteric glands. In cases where the lungs themselves have been diseased, it is observable that they are sometimes in a disposition to let the mischief spread in a rapid manner all over them, and in a very short time become a fatal consumption; while in other instances the injured part of the lungs has seemed to remain in the same state for twenty, forty, or even sixty years, with very little inconvenience beside the cough, so that the patient

has grown fat with it; or else the disease of the
lungs has spread so slowly, that though the
cough has become a little worse every winter
from youth to old age, yet it has not been till
towards the end of a long life, that the lungs
have become so diseased, as to do their duty
with that difficulty, which is called an asthma.
Even an ulcer of the lungs, as was judged from
the blood and purulent liquor spit up, has for a
considerable time kept itself confined within
the same bounds.   In a few cases the ulcer has
probably been seated in a capsula, which has at
last been coughed up with great efforts, and
some danger of suffocation; after which there
has been a total cessation of all the complaints,
the sore being in all probability entirely healed.
In hysteric, and convulsive diseases, arising from
some disordered state of the whole system of
nerves, those serving to respiration have among
the rest been disturbed so as to occasion violent
coughs, without any more injury to the lungs,
than the convulsions of the limbs, or body, occasion in those parts, which they have seized.
These coughs, and those arising from defluxions
upon the lungs, are attended sometimes with
an unusual noise, and are generally much
stronger, than consumptive coughs are, not
only in their beginning, but even in their ad-

vanced state. The same is likewise the case with those coughs, which are owing to some hard body fallen into the trachea. I have seen a violent, and almost perpetual cough, arising from a bone fixed in the wind-pipe, which had lasted some months with an unusual sound, and presently ceased upon coughing up the bone.

Coughs have molested some persons alternately with ophthalmies, the gout, scald head, and other cutaneous disorders. It must be remembered that in all long coughs there is danger of a consumption, and therefore a cool regimen is of indispensable use, in order to keep the lungs in that state, which is most likely to hinder the sound parts from being infected by the diseased. There have been too many examples of coughs remaining in a tolerable state for twenty years, and which with proper care might have remained so for twenty more, which have by mismanagement, or catching cold, been joined by all the symptoms of a quick consumption, soon terminating in death. Hence arises a difficulty of deciding, whether a cough be a consumptive one: most coughs naturally tend to a pulmonary phthisis; and though the tendency be sometimes so strong, that there is no hazard of being mistaken in pronouncing the cough consumptive, yet in many instances no physician can prognosticate the event, unless he be able to predict also what the patient's manner of living will be, and whether he will always escape violent colds, and peripneumonies.

Abstemiousness, change of air, and a judicious use both of bleeding, and of opium, have proved the best means of soothing a troublesome cough, and of hindering it from becoming a dangerous one.

CHAP. 93.

Tussis convulsiva.

THE hooping-cough is most common among children, and is undoubtedly contagious: it is a tedious disorder, lasting often for several months; and though sometimes slight, yet in some children it proves fatal. An inundation of phlegm, or a vomiting, the clearness of the intervals, and the violence of the fits, may generally distinguish it from a common cough in the very beginning; but afterwards it cannot be mistaken, when the expiration in coughing continues so long, that they can hardly recover the power of drawing in their breath, which is done at last with a peculiar sound, called hooping; and this principally characterises this dis-

temper. A child has had one of these coughs
three months before the hooping came on. The
violence of the cough sometimes makes the
nose bleed, and the face blackish, and has
strained the eyes so as to do them a lasting injury. It does not usually attack a person more
than once; but to this I have heard some few
exceptions among those whom I have attended in it, of whom more than one have assured me they had been ill of it before.

Old persons are less liable to this malady, but
by no means exempt from it: I have seen it
in a woman of seventy, and in a man of four-
score. A child has some notice of the approach of a fit, so as to be able to run to his
nurse, or mother, before it begins; but adults
are, as it were, overpowered at once upon the
access of the fit, so that they fall down instantly,
as in an apoplexy, but very soon come to themselves: this is a distinguishing symptom of the
disease in those who are grown up; and if they
have not before been subject to a cough, and
have lately been in the way of catching this
distemper, the circumstance of their falling
down in this manner may take away all doubt
about the nature of their illness. Flatulence in
an extraordinary degree often accompanies this
cough.

Experience has instructed us, that a change of air is of singular use in abating the force, and shortening the stay of this distemper. The stomach is so much disordered in it by being overloaded with phlegm and oppressed with wind, that it seems very reasonable to relieve and strengthen this part by the help of rhubarb and bitters. The hooping-cough has so much the nature of a convulsion, that a prudent use of opium, together with musk, lac ammoniaci, and vinum antimonii, might probably be beneficial; but I have not seen such undoubted success from these medicines, as to be confident of their virtues. As for the numberless specifics, which are every where to be met with, I have nothing to say in their favour from my own observation.

CHAP. 94.

Valetudo conquassata.

A DANGEROUS disease, or great decay of the parts necessary to life, occasions what is called a broken state of health; by which is meant an assemblage of many or most of the following complaints: A paleness, or sallowness of the countenance; a bloated face; thirst; shortness of breath; palpitation of the heart; flatulence;

loathing of food; sickness; frequent making of water; incontinence of the stools, and of the urine; swelling of the legs; wandering pains; spasms; wasting of the flesh; weakness; lassitude; itching of the skin; tremblings; numbnesses; feverishness; languor; faintings; sleepiness in the day-time; want of sleep at night; forgetfulness.

Chap. 95.

Variolæ.

The experience which I have had of inoculation, does not enable me to add any thing to what has been already established in relation to its utility, or the management of the inoculated. I am sorry to have found, that this operation has not always secured the patient from having the small-pox afterwards, if the eruption have been imperfect without maturation. I attended one in a very full small-pox, which ran through all its stages in the usual manner; yet this person had been inoculated ten years before, and on the fifth day after inoculation began to be feverish with a headach followed by a slight eruption, which eruption soon went off without coming to suppuration: the place of inoculation had inflamed, and remained open ten days, leaving a deep scar, which I saw.

By some accident, most of the notes are lost, which had been made during my attendance on a great number of patients in the uninoculated small-pox; therefore I shall not attempt to give a full history of this distemper, but confine myself to the relating of such observations as are justified by the few remaining papers.

Many instances have occurred to me, which shew that one who has never had the small-pox, may safely associate, and even lie in the same bed with a variolous patient, for the two or three first days of the eruption, without any danger of receiving the infection. One woman continued to suckle her infant for two days after the small-pox had begun to appear upon her; and the child being then removed escaped the distemper for that time, but was unquestionably capable of being infected, because he catched it about a year and half after.

Parents have several times judged it proper, when one of their children has fallen ill of the small-pox, not to send those away, who had not had this distemper, but to let them all continue together in the same house, and often in the same chamber. About the sixth day after the distemper had arrived at its height in the sick child, the others have for the most part begun to complain; and therefore it is probable that this is the time, when the distemper begins to be communicable; the infection lying dormant about the same number of days, that it does in those who have been inoculated. But there are much greater varieties in this way of taking the small-pox, than by inoculation, accordingly as persons go more or less into the way of receiving the breath of the sick person, or of touching things daubed with the variolous matter. Two children were constantly kept in the sick chamber, and yet did not fall ill till a month after; and there are not a few examples of persons, who have seemed to be equally exposed to the infection, and yet have received it at different times.

An excruciating pain in the loins has never failed to be succeeded by a bad small-pox; and the more violent the pain, the greater has been the danger: it is much safer to have it between the shoulders; but it is safest to have none in any part of the back.

Excessive vomiting for the whole time before the eruption is seldom followed by a mild disease; and if the vomiting be continued after the eruption is completed, the patient's life is in great danger, even though the small-pox be not confluent, as I have seen more than once.

It is very common to have convulsions precede a mild small-pox in children, and the same has been known in some adults with as prosperous an event.

The variolous infection does some force to the vessels, which supply the menstrual discharge in women; and in the worst sort of small-pox this evacuation has come on out of its regular course two days before the small-pox has begun to shew itself, and has continued to flow in an excessive manner. It has sometimes appeared before its regular time, together with the eruption. But what I have more usually observed is, that this uterine flux in almost all female patients has begun as soon as the eruption was completed, and it has continued from one day to five. This discharge, though sometimes much greater than the natural one, does not seem to check the progress of the small-pox, nor to sink the patient's strength, and therefore very little pains need be taken to stop it, even though we had any ready and innocent way of doing it.

That very formidable symptom, bloody urine, has come on about the fifth day from the first sickness; the eruption in the mean time has hardly risen above the skin, chiefly shewing itself in purple spots and blotches, and resembling variolous pimples only in very few places. The stools are likewise bloody; the very tears have been like lotura carnium; and if a small scratch has any where been made in the skin, the blood has for many hours continued to ooze out, and has hardly been stopped. This hopeless state has been terminated by death in three or four days after the eruption; nor have I remarked one exception. But the urine may be discoloured in the small-pox, and have a hue as dark as coffee, even where there is no reason to suspect its proceeding from gravel, and yet afford no ground for alarm, if not joined with other bad symptoms. In a middling sort of small-pox, the urine became black on the fourth day of the eruption, and continued so for four days. In another, the same black urine began on the second day of the sickness, having a sediment like coffee-grounds for two days. Both these patients went on prosperously, without any other bad or unusual symptom. The pustules have sometimes shewn themselves not very different from their general appearance in a middling sort; but the interstices have been filled with small round purple spots, and the distemper has been fatal on the third day of the eruption.

It has been remarked above, that the variolous virus has a peculiar effect in exciting the uterine flux, and upon this property of it perhaps depends its well-known effect upon pregnant women, who usually miscarry on the seventh or eighth day from the first eruption, and in a day or two after die. The fœtus of this abortion I have often examined with great attention. The skin of it has been much discoloured, in some parts of a dirty red, in others blackish, and in a few places of a natural colour; but I never could see any appearance of a variolous eruption. I have known a very few pregnant women, who have gone through this distemper without miscarrying, and have afterwards been brought to bed at the natural time; but I could never see upon these children any such marks as might be left by a variolous eruption; and I am well assured, that such children have afterwards had the small-pox. A young girl was opened, who died full of the small-pox, and I observed that none of the bowels or internal parts shewed the least marks of their having any variolous pustules: now the fœtus in utero seems to be so much in the same state with the bowels, that if these are never the seat of the pustules, it is hardly to be expected that any should be found upon the fœtus.

A great shortness of breath coming on about the fifth day of the eruption, scarcely leaves any hopes that the patient will survive the distemper. The difficulty of breathing is sometimes so great, as not to suffer the patient to lie down, or to have breath sufficient for speaking a common sentence.

A sudden sinking of the swelling in the face, so that the eyes can be opened; an abrupt stoppage of the spitting; a frequent wanting to make water, and making of very little at a time; a total absence of all fœtor; and great shiverings; though they be very dangerous signs, yet have been seen without proving fatal.

Watery bladders full of a yellow serum, like those raised by blistering plasters, rise up among the pustules in some kinds of the small-pox, and may shew an irregularity and malignity; but such patients have recovered.

In the decline of the distemper, when most of the scabs had fallen off, I have twice seen a few pimples with watery heads, without any redness or inflammation, which afterwards maturated and resembled the true small-pox. These pustules were only in the soles of the feet and palms of the hands. In one child the pocks were large, and few, for four days, and then there was an eruption of very small and numerous pustules, from which the child with difficulty escaped. In another there were a few pocks, and the child notwithstanding was very restless and oppressed: after these were dried, others broke out, and came to maturation; and even afterwards one or two made their appearance. The child died, though all the pocks, if they had appeared together, were so few, that I never saw any other person die, who had not more. These are the only instances, which have occurred to me something like, what is often talked of, a second crop.

It has happened to three variolous patients in the decline of their distemper, when they were thinking of having a little meat allowed, and of taking, as usual, some purging medicine, that they have suddenly become gloomy and suspicious, and in forty-eight hours have died raving mad.

An excessive spitting, which proves so beneficial in the confluent small-pox, has in a few persons continued for several days after the decline of the distemper, in a degree equal to a common salivation, and no harm has ensued.

The milk of a woman, who suckled a child, began to lessen at the height of the small-pox, and soon after went quite away; but after a few days it returned as plentiful as ever.

In all distempers it is considered as a favorable circumstance, that the person is free from all other complaints, with a constitution naturally good, and unimpaired: for when there is nothing to divert the powers of life from opposing the present illness with their whole force, a happy event may reasonably be expected: and yet a complication of the small-pox with other formidable maladies, has in several instances not exalted its malignity, or produced a bad sort, nor disabled the patient from struggling through it in the usual manner. Venereal distempers have often been joined by a mild small-pox; and in a worse sort they have not at all added to the usual danger or sufferings of the patient. Others have catched the small-pox, when they were dying of scrofulous consumptions; but have still had all the necessary strength to recover unhurt from the new distemper, and they have not appeared to die a day the sooner of their old one.

In a large town, at a time when agues were epidemical, it chanced that the small-pox was brought in, and many catched it before they were cured of their agues. It was observable, that the ague stopped spontaneously in these patients, as soon as the small-pox fever began, and constantly returned after the small-pox was over and one or two purges had been taken. The two distempers seemed to have no other influence over one another.

Mankind has hitherto been blessed with specifics for very few distempers. The small-pox is one among many others, the proper remedy for which, if there be one, is left to be found out by the sagacity, or good fortune, of future physicians. Sanguine expectations have been entertained of the great service, which the Peruvian bark, and the preparations of antimony, and of mercury, would do in opposing the variolous virus. But such hopes have upon trial all dwindled away, and left us just where we were. The method therefore of treating the small-pox will not differ from that which is contained in the general doctrine of the regimen and diet of the sick: and the troublesome symptoms, which may arise, must be relieved, and the functions of life kept as much as possible in their natural state, by the same means, which are used in any other fever. Costiveness in particular is as hurtful in the variolous fever, as in any other: which I mention, because the contrary opinion formerly prevailed, and is hardly yet quite worn out.

Variolæ Pusillæ. *The Chicken-Pox.*

THE chicken-pox and swine-pox differ, I believe, only in name; they occasion so little danger or trouble to the patients, that physicians are seldom sent for to them, and have therefore very few opportunities of seeing this distemper. Hence it happens that the name of it is met with in very few books, and hardly any pretend to say a word of its history.

But though it be so insignificant an illness, that an acquaintance with it is not of much use for its own sake, yet it is of importance on account of the small-pox, with which it may otherwise be confounded, and so deceive the persons, who have had it, into a false security, which may prevent them either from keeping out of the way of the small-pox, or from being inoculated. For this reason I have judged it might be useful to contribute, what I have learned from experience, towards its description.

These pocks break out in many without any illness or previous sign: in others they are preceded by a little degree of chillness, lassitude, cough, broken sleep, wandering pains, loss of appetite, and feverishness for three days.

In some patients I have observed them to make their first appearance on the back, but this perhaps is not constant. Most of them are of the common size of the small-pox, but some are less. I never saw them confluent, nor very numerous. The greatest number, which I ever observed, was about twelve in the face, and two hundred over the rest of the body.

On the first day of the eruption they are reddish. On the second day there is at the top of most of them a very small bladder, about the size of a millet-seed. This is sometimes full of a watery and colourless, sometimes of a yellowish liquor, contained between the cuticle and skin. On the second, or, at the farthest, on the third day from the beginning of the eruption, as many of these pocks, as are not broken, seem arrived at their full maturity; and those, which are fullest of that yellow liquor, very much resemble what the genuine small-pox are on the fifth or sixth day, especially where there happens to be a larger space than ordinary occupied by the extravasated serum. It happens to most of them, either on the first day that this little bladder arises, or on the day after, that its tender cuticle is burst by the accidental rubbing of the clothes, or by the patient's hands to allay the itching which attends this eruption. A thin scab is then formed at the top of the pock, and the swelling of the other part abates, without its ever being turned into pus, as it is in the small-pox. Some few escape being burst; and the little drop of liquor contained in the vesicle at the top of them grows yellow and thick, and dries into a scab. On the fifth day of the eruption they are almost all dried and covered with a slight crust. The inflammation of these pocks is very small, and the contents of them do not seem to be owing to suppuration, as in the small-pox, but rather to what is extravasated immediately under the cuticle by the serous vessels of the skin, as in a common blister. No wonder therefore that this liquor appears so soon as on the second day, and that upon the cuticle being broken it is presently succeeded by a slight scab: hence too, as the true skin is so little affected, no mark or scar is likely to be left, unless in one or two pocks, where, either by being accidentally much fretted, or by some extraordinary sharpness of the contents, a little ulcer is formed in the skin.

The patients scarce suffer any thing throughout the whole progress of this illness, except some languidness of strength and spirits and appetite, all which may probably be owing to the confining of themselves to their chamber. I saw two children ill of the chicken-pox, whose mother chose to be with them, though she had never had this illness. Upon the eighth or ninth day after the pocks were at their height in the children, the mother fell ill of this distemper then beginning to shew itself. In this instance the infection lay in the body much about the same time that it is known to do in the small-pox.

, Remedies are not likely to be much wanted in a disease attended with hardly any inconvenience, and which in so short a time is certainly cured of itself.

The principal marks, by which the chicken-pox may be distinguished from the small-pox, are,

1. The appearance on the second or third day from the eruption of that vesicle full of serum upon the top of the pock.

2. The crust, which covers the pocks on the fifth day; at which time those of the small-pox are not at the height of their suppuration.

Foreign medical writers hardly ever mention the name of this distemper; and the writers of

our own country scarce mention any thing
more of it, than in name. Morton speaks of
it as if he supposed it to be a very mild genuine
small-pox. But these two distempers are surely
totally different from one another, not only on
account of their different appearances above
mentioned, but because those, who have had
the small-pox, are capable of being infected
with the chicken-pox; but those, who have
once had the chicken-pox, are not capable of
having it again, though to such, as have never
had this distemper, it seems as infectious as the
small-pox. I wetted a thread in the most con-
cocted pus-like liquor of the chicken-pox,
which I could find; and after making a slight
incision, it was confined upon the arm of one
who had formerly had it; the little wound
healed up immediately, and shewed no signs
of any infection. From the great similitude
between the two distempers, it is probable, that,
instead of the small-pox, some persons have
been inoculated from the chicken-pox, and
that the distemper which has succeeded, has
been mistaken for the small-pox by hasty or
unexperienced observers.

There is sometimes seen an eruption, concerning which I have been in doubt, whether
it be one of the many unnoticed cutaneous dis-

eases, or only, as I am rather inclined to believe, a more malignant sort of chicken-pox.

This disorder is preceded for three or four
days by all the symptoms which forerun the
chicken-pox, but in a much higher degree.
On the fourth or fifth day the eruption appears,
with very little abatement of the fever; the
pains likewise of the limbs and back still continue, to which are joined pains of the gums.
The pocks are redder than the chicken-pocks,
and spread wider, and hardly rise so high, at
least not in proportion to their size. Instead of
one little head or vesicle of a serous matter, these
have from four to ten or twelve. They go off
just like the chicken-pox, and are distinguish-
able from the small-pox by the same marks;
besides which the continuance of the pains
and fever after the eruption, and the degree of
both these, though there be not above twenty
pocks, are, as far as I have seen, what never
happen in the small-pox.

Many foreigners seem so little to have attended to the peculiar characteristics of the
small-pox, particularly the length of time,
which it requires to its full maturation, that we
may the less wonder at the prevailing opinion
among them, that the same person is liable to

have it several times. Petrus Borellus* records
the case of a woman, who had this distemper
seven times, and catching it again died of it the
eighth time. It would be no extravagant as-
sertion to say, that here in England not above
one in ten thousand patients is pretended to
have had it twice; and wherever it is pretended, it will always be as likely that the persons
about the patient were mistaken, and supposed
that to be the small-pox, which was an eruption
of a different nature, as that there was such an
extraordinary exception to what we are sure is
so general a law.

Chap. 97.

Ventriculi Morbi.

One among the many disorders of the stomach is a disagreeable sense of acidity rising
from it, which is accompanied often with pain,
or a sort of anxiety worse than pain, sickness
and vomiting, a sense of weight, voraciousness
in some, and loss of appetite in others, flatulence, and distension of the stomach, head-ach,
great quantities of phlegm, and a waking out
of sleep with some degree of terror.

* Hist. and Obs. Rar. Med. Phys. centur. iii. obs. 10.

If we were to reason upon chemical principles, nothing seems more practicable, than to neutralise, and subdue an acid, to which we can immediately add whatever we think proper; but the animating principle makes so much difference between a living stomach and an inanimate vessel, that this, which appears easy in theory, has been found very difficult in practice; and persons have been teased with this complaint for twenty years, without being able to find a cure. Lime water, magnesia, testaceous powders in the quantity of an ounce every day, and alkaline salts, have in several instances been tried in vain.

Milk, vegetables, fish, fat of any kind, a full meal, especially with any exercise soon after it, have generally disagreed with stomachs disposed to acidities, which they have much increased. Acids themselves have not always been hurtful, but have sometimes proved a relief. Emetics and Bath waters have succeeded with some, and failed with others. Large quantities of testaceous powders, and rhubarb, have been the most generally useful; a costive habit of body has been always prejudicial. After trying a variety of means for many years upon the most unconquerably acid stomach which I ever knew, the method, in which the patient settled, and which alone was able to keep the complaint in tolerable order, was the taking one ounce of testaceous powders every morning, and drinking a gallon of warm water, as an emetic, every night; which course, with a little rhubarb occasionally, was pursued for several years.

The heartburn is an usual companion of acidities in the stomach, differing very little from them, either in its causes, or cure, and has been as obstinate in resisting all sorts of medicines. It has been attended with hiccups, eructations, and an immoderate flow of saliva. During pregnancy it is apt to be uncommonly troublesome, and is often added to the evils of the gout, and sometimes to those of the jaundice. A disposition to it seems to be born with some persons, who have been teased with this uneasy sensation for the greatest part of their lives. Cutaneous eruptions, and the heartburn, have alternately harassed some persons. One woman, while she was breeding, could find no relief for a violent heartburn from any of the usual remedies, and was at last cured by elixir of vitriol.

§ 2. *Ventriculi Dolor.*

Inflammations, or cancerous scirrhi of the

liver, spleen, and pancreas, with all other
kinds of pains between the breast and the navel,
are usually referred to the stomach; and beside
the disorders, which properly belong to it, and
have their origin there, it sympathises with all
parts of the body in many of their ails. The
gout, and perhaps the rheumatism, wandering
pains, and those that are fixed, all sores and
cutaneous diseases, have frequently either de-
serted their first seats and fallen upon the stomach, or else have drawn it to suffer together
with the parts first affected. With regard to
giddinesses, and head-achs, though they be
sometimes the causes, yet they seem oftener
the effects of stomach disorders. The diseases
of the womb injure the stomach in a very remarkable manner; and it rarely escapes without pain, or sickness, whenever any of the
various irregularities of the menstrua are complained of. It is equally a sufferer in hysteric
and hypochondriac maladies, in all great per-
turbations of mind, and in worms, even those
which are generally found only in the great
intestines.

Where there is no reason to suspect and
provide against any of these causes, and where
the pain does not proceed from any poison, or
improper food; if it be very excessive by fits,

with intervals, especially very long ones, of perfect ease and blameless health, there we have the greatest reason to believe it owing to gall-stones. I have noted a very considerable number of persons, who for many years (some not less than twenty) had been subject to returns of pains in what is called the pit of the stomach, and at last the appearance of the jaundice clearly pointed out their origin, or the voiding of a gall-stone has entirely removed them. In others, after a fit of the jaundice, the same pain which preceded it, and had given the patients too much reason not to mistake it, has continued to torment them at irregular times, sometimes without a yellowness, and sometimes with, for at least twelve years. Some have been subject for a great part of their lives to a moderate or dull pain in the side, or about the stomach, which, as I judged from the appearances after death, upon their being opened, was most probably owing to some gentler movements of a gall-stone.

The great variety of pains attributed to the stomach, and the different causes of those which truly belong to it, will account for the variety of their concomitant symptoms, and the different events of similar treatments.

Bath, wine, hot medicines, a full stomach,

a vegetable diet, cathartics, emetics, the state of pregnancy, a fit of the gout, acids, worm-medicines, blisters to the region of the stomach; all these have in many instances been found to do good, to do harm, and to do nothing at all. After due attention has been used to discover the true nature of the pain, if there be reason to think that its origin is in the stomach, and that it does not proceed from any inflammatory or scirrhous affection, an emetic is generally useful at first, and afterwards the method of cure, which has often succeeded, is either the drinking of Bath water, or a daily use of some of the bitter and aromatic simples, joined with as much rhubarb, or aloes, as may be necessary to keep off all tendency to costiveness. A teaspoonful of some aromatic tincture has likewise been taken with great advantage in a little water immediately after dinner.

A great variety of such medicines is to be found in all pharmacopœïas, out of which such may be chosen as will suit most stomachs, and hardly offend any palates. They are of frequent and very important use in the practice of physic, not only because the disorders of this part are far more common than those of any other, but because in unknown distempers, or in those where there is no good to be done by evacuations, and for which we have no specifics, we can only aim at putting the general health into the best state possible, the principal means of doing which will be to strengthen the stomach.

§ 3. *Morbi Lienis.*

A man in his fiftieth year began to lose his flesh and strength with some degree of fever. He sometimes felt slight shiverings, and sometimes very strong ones, returning irregularly during the whole illness. His appetite was lost, but he had no vomiting. The stools were regular till the two last months of his life. The urine was in a natural state. The pulse was very rarely too quick. There was no tension of the belly. In the second month of his illness he had an excessive pain in his stomach. Pains of the loins, hips, and back, would come on suddenly, without continuing above half an hour. For a few days his right hand was swelled, and in pain; and for two days the calf of the left leg was too painful to bear being touched, but without any heat, redness, or swelling. He complained chiefly of the right side of the belly. During the last two months of his life he was harassed with an unconquerable diarrhœa. This illness proved fatal about the sixth month.

A large ulcer was found in one part of the spleen, and the rest of it seemed rotten. An adhesion had been formed between the spleen and peritonæum. No other parts were distempered.

A man forty-two years old had complained for several months of loss of appetite, flatulence, white stools, dark coloured urine, frequent bloody stools, tenesmus, perpetual nausea and attempts to vomit, chiefly in an empty stomach, excessive restlessness, want of sleep, bleedings at the nose, thirst, and light-headedness, though the fever was moderate. At last a sudden vomiting of blood came on; which returning in five hours, put an end to his life. The spleen was found of an uncommon magnitude, but without hardness; the inside of it was all dissolved into a bloody sanies. The glands of the mesentery were full of the same matter. The liver was sound. The portion of the stomach nearest to the spleen was inflamed; and there were signs of inflammation in many parts of the intestines.

A woman was languishing for six months

with a failure of appetite, and a swelling of the left side of the belly. There then came on sickness, and pain of the stomach, a total loss of appetite, a diarrhœa with great pain, which could not be stopped, and extreme restlessness, which lasted about six months longer. The spleen weighed fifty-two ounces, but was not ulcered, or scirrhous. The intestines were in a natural state, and there was no water in the abdomen.

§ 4. *Morbi Pancreatis.*

A woman had long been afflicted with a pain, as she said, of her stomach; which was excessive for the last year of her life. She had no appetite, and what she did get down was vomited up. She could hardly procure any sleep. The pancreas was found scirrhous.

Another woman, whose pancreas was scirrhous, had complained for seven years of a pain in her stomach, and of pains in her bowels, and hips; a numbness of her thigh and leg, with a sense of cold; loss of appetite, and frequent acid vomitings*.

* A man, twenty-three years of age, had been afflicted for five months with pains in the bowels, upon the ceasing of which the stomach swelled, and there came on indigestion, a diminution of the quantity of urine, and weakness which gradually increased;

CHAP. 98.

Vertigo.

A VERTIGO, giddiness, or swimming of the head, is a disorder incident to both sexes; from which young persons, especially females, are not secure, though it be far more frequently found in the old and infirm.

From a consideration of the cases, which I have had an opportunity of observing, it seems probable, that many vertigos have arisen from disorders of the stomach, more still from those of the head, but most of all from general weakness. If I were to judge from the ages, the constitutions, the juvantia and lædentia, there is a very inconsiderable number of vertiginous complaints, which can be attributed to a fulness of blood, and too high health ; therefore in cases, in which there may be reason to suspect a plethora, we should proceed with caution, and feel out our way by observing how the first moderate evacuants were borne, and be guided accordingly in determining the de-

lastly, a purging that could not be restrained. In the third month from the swelling of the stomach this man died. The pancreas was found enlarged to an enormous size, and ulcerated. *E.*

gree of strength, and the number of repetitions, which we may afterwards venture to use.

Want of appetite, indigestion, flatulence, pain and weight in the stomach, sickness, vomiting, costiveness, and worms, have been found either to precede, or to be joined with a swimming of the head. Now, where some of these make either the only, or the principal complaints, next to the giddiness, we may reasonably conclude, that the head is affected only secondarily, and that the original seat of the disorder is in the stomach.

Tormenting head-achs, a lightness of the head, deafness, a singing in the ears, objects appearing double, temporary blindness, mists, black spots, or sparks and flashes of fire before the eyes, bleedings at the nose, hypochondriac and hysteric maladies, epileptic, paralytic, or apoplectic fits, lethargy, spasms, and convulsions (many of which are often united with vertigos), are all such manifest affections of the head, that where these predominate, the giddiness probably has its origin in the brain.

Lastly, a vertigo has been accompanied with languor, tremblings, faintings, and palpitations, and has supervened inveterate gouts, obstinate intermittents, asthmas, and other long disorders, profuse bleedings, and diarrhœas, and has often made one of the train of evils belonging to a state of health much injured by the obstruction of some customary evacuation, as the menstrua, piles, sores, and cutaneous disorders, or utterly broken by intemperance, diseases, or old age. Nor is it unknown, that a vertigo should be the single complaint, the health being in all other respects unimpaired.

Where there is satisfactory proof that the vertigo is dependent upon some other disorder, the most reasonable manner of endeavouring to cure it will be by removing the primary complaint. But it must be owned, that it is often difficult, from the strange complication of symptoms, to decide what is the precise nature of the giddiness, or to account for the different events of remedies in circumstances apparently the same.

By the notes, which I have taken, it appears, that a spontaneous vomiting and diarrhœa have always been beneficial; that snuff, too much business and fatigue, a crowd, the first waking in a morning, stooping, standing, walking, turning in bed, and any alteration of posture, hot weather, a warm climate, fasting, and evacuations, have generally tended to bring on, or to aggravate a swimming of the head: that cupping, a discharge by the piles, bleeding by leeches, or by the lancet, blisters, cutaneous eruptions, emetics, issues, cold bathing, and the gout, have sometimes been judged to relieve a vertigo; but that many of them have been far oftener useless, especially the gout, and blisters; but bleeding by the lancet, and strong cathartics have appeared to do harm much more frequently than good, and in most instances have at best been useless. If Bath waters have been innocent in this malady, they have never given me reason to think them beneficial. Cupping has often failed in relieving a present fit, but it has in several instances been singularly useful in preventing the returns, or in greatly mitigating their violence, by being used every two months, about six ounces of blood being taken away each time.

The danger attending a vertigo, and the difficulty of relieving it, are to be estimated from its having no concomitant ails, or from their kind and number. Where it is accompanied with such as arise from the stomach, and especially if there be but a few of them, it is then more easily remedied, than when it is joined with affections of the head, the cure of which is tedious and uncertain. However, in hypochondriac and hysteric cases, the danger of a vertigo is not much, though it may not be easily removed. But if the giddiness be only one of the many evils, of which an irreparably broken state of health consists, what hope can there be of a cure?

A vertigo unconnected with any symptoms of other diseases may probably be brought on by causes of too little importance to create any danger, or much disturbance to the general health; for such a vertigo, though considerable enough in some young men to endanger their falling, has not hindered their outliving it, and arriving at a healthy old age; and several have been frequently troubled with it for twenty, or even thirty years, with good health in all other respects.

CHAP. 99.
Vomitus*.

A DISPOSITION to vomiting is very various in different constitutions: some cannot be made to vomit by any means; others not without extreme difficulty, and great pain; while several are prompted to it upon the slightest occasions, and it costs them not the least trouble. I have seen one, who performed a sort of rumination;

* See chap. 65, concerning *nausea*, or *sickness of the stomach*.

and if the food staid too long in his stomach, before it was returned back for this purpose, it became sour, and made him sick, and was vomited up.

Vomiting seems so contrary to nature, that experience alone could satisfy us of the possibility of its being continued, as I have known it, two or three times a day for many months, or many years, with little, or no ill consequences to the health. One woman told me she had for thirty years vomited up all she had taken. In some cases, though all the food seemed to be vomited up, yet the patients have thriven, and grown fat. In pregnancy many women have judged that they brought up more than the whole of what had been swallowed, and that for a considerable time, without endangering the life either of the mother, or the child.

In hard drinkers, and breeding women, the morning is the most usual time of vomiting; this has likewise happened, though rarely, in some sober men; but in general it is either soon, or a few hours after eating, that the sickness comes on, which ends in throwing up the contents of the stomach.

The stomach is secondarily affected by sympathizing, in a great many disorders, with other parts of the body; and it has many ails peculiar to itself, which hinder it from receiving, or retaining what has been swallowed: some of these are manifest after death, as scirrhous obstructions of the cardia, or pylorus: there are many others connected with the unknown powers of the stomach, which occasion no alteration of its appearance after death, as far as our senses are able to judge, there being no more traces of them left, than of a nausea or vomiting excited by sudden ill news, or the sight or remembrance of disgustful objects. I remember one, who for many years had been subject to a vomiting of almost all his food, and often of great quantities of blood, whose stomach after death shewed no signs of any disorder, though it was examined by some very experienced and skilful anatomists.

The matter thrown up by vomiting has been sometimes the food unchanged, sometimes a salt or acid liquor, or phlegm, and by great straining a little bile will be pumped into the stomach, and thence brought up. A fat, inflammable matter, has often been forced up by mouthfuls not long after eating; and lastly blood, or a liquor deeply tinged with blood, has been vomited frequently, and in great abundance, for several days together, with extreme loss of strength; or else has returned, more like a chronical affection, in a slighter degree, two or three times a year for several years; and though it have relieved a pain of the stomach, yet even this chronical sort must always be considered as the symptom of a dangerous disorder of this part. The apparent quantity of blood voided from the stomach upon these occasions is very alarming, and would be much more so, if it were not probable that blood itself makes often the least part of the bloody liquor which has been thrown up. Bloody, or black stools, have always accompanied a vomiting of blood. Some have had several returns of vomiting blood, and apparently in large quantities, for several years; and in others their first vomiting of blood has in two or three days ended in death. I know of no treatment required for this sort of hæmorrhage different from what is mentioned in the Medical Transactions, vol. ii. Query 4. The necessity of keeping the patient quiet, and calm, and cool, appeared very strongly in one case, where the least drop of wine, warming the hands at the fire, putting them into warm water, a warmed bed, a blister, a purge, and any ruffle or disturbance of mind, were often experienced to renew the bleeding.

For other vomitings I have taken notice that purging, riding, and fat of every kind, have been prejudicial; that the spontaneous clearing of the stomach has given no relief; that an emetic has sometimes failed, or even aggravated the complaint; I was told by one person, that he had the patience to persevere in the use of emetics, till he had taken near forty, without any success. However, an emetic has very generally proved serviceable : it seems better calculated to relieve a sudden sickness, than to cure an old habitual vomiting. Bath waters have been remarkably efficacious in curing the morning sickness of hard-drinkers; but has failed in many other cases of sickness. The anodyne balsam rubbed in upon the stomach, has been very successful; and so likewise has a blister applied to the region of the stomach. Acids have been useful to some of these patients, and the alkaline salts and testaceous powders to others. One person was cured by leaving off the use of bread; and another by drinking water cooled by ice. But it must happen that these and all other means will fail in stopping a sickness and vomiting, which arises, as it has often done, from incurable disorders of the stomach or neighbouring bowels.

CHAP. 100.

Vox.

THE voice without any pain, or other disorder of the health, has been weakened so as
never to rise above a whisper. In a slight degree of this complaint the persons are able to
laugh in the usual manner; but they are sometimes as incapable of laughing, as of speaking,
loud. Those, who have once experienced such
a failure of voice, have been very subject to
relapses. They have lost their voices suddenly
without any previous notice, and recovered
them as quickly without any apparent cause.
Nine out of ten of those, whom I have seen in
this complaint, have been women, and most
of them, but not all, have been young and
puny, or hysteric, or old and infirm.

An inability to speak beyond a weak whisper
has frequently lasted for many months, and in
some for several years in the same uniform
manner. Others have lost their voices only for
the morning, or afternoon of every day; or
for a certain number of months in every year.
Sea bathing, and blisters, have been supposed
to do some little service. Internal stimulants,
and evacuants, have hardly been innocent;

they have certainly been useless, and so have all other means which I have tried.

The sudden weakness of voice, of which I have been speaking, is very different from that hoarseness, which belongs to bad coughs, asthmas, and catarrhs.

CHAP. 101.

Urina.*

AN eager desire of making water has been considered under the article of Stranguria, and Prostatæ Scirrhus, and Calculus. Beside the causes there mentioned, it has been an attendant upon a scirrhous spleen, and upon hysteric and paralytic maladies, and has been one of the infirmities of old age, where there has been no other distemper. It has been very troublesome to several in the night, so as greatly to interrupt their rest; and it has teased others only in the day time, suffering them to rest quietly in the night.

A difficulty of expelling the urine has not only arisen from the causes mentioned under Stranguria, and Ischuria, but also from a pa-

----

* See *Calculus, Graviditas, Ischuria,* and *Stranguria.*

ralytic inability of the muscles which should
expel it. In one man the catheter was necessary for this purpose during the space of two
years, after which the parts recovered their use,
and the inconvenience ceased.

The colour of the urine has been milky in a
diseased prostate gland, and in other cases,
where it might be owing to some purulent
liquor with which it was mixed.

A large suppuration of an inflamed sore
throat has been attended with a considerable
quantity of pus at the bottom of the vessel
which held the urine, for three or four days.
As soon as the abscess broke and discharged
itself, this purulent appearance in the urine
ceased. This is the only instance that has occurred to me of any thing like a translation of
matter from other parts to the kidneys.

In some broken constitutions, whenever
water was made, there has followed a great
languor, or sickness of the stomach.

An ulcer of the womb has in several women
pierced the rectum and the bladder, so that
wind and fæces would come away with their
urine. An ulcer, probably of the prostate
gland, has had the same effect in men: and
one person believed that the breach between

the bladder and rectum had been the consequence of efforts occasioned by excessive costiveness.

A stone in the bladder, a diseased prostate,
the fluor albus, frequent miscarriages, and some
rough or pungent liquors, have occasioned a
heat of urine, where there was no reason to
suspect a Venereal cause.

The bladder is naturally defended from the
sharpness of the urine by a mucous substance
with which it is lined. All irritation, from
whatever cause it may arise, increases this glairy
matter, which will adhere to the vessel into
which it is made, like starch. It is very different from true pus, which settles at the bottom
of the urine like cream; both these appearances have been found to arise from irritation
joined with some inflammation, without any
ulcer : there will at the same time be more or
less eagerness to make water, and pain in
making it, according to the degree and cause
of the irritation. A diseased prostate gland,
inflammations or ulcers of any of the urinary
passages, strictures of the urethra, frequent
Venereal injuries, and the stone, or gravel, have
been the common sources of these appearances
in the urine. If the purulent liquor be consi-

derable in quantity, mixed with streaks of blood, and fetid, while the neck of the bladder is in a natural state, it may probably be conjectured that there is an ulcer of the kidney, but of this it is hard to form a certain judgment.

An incontinence of urine, though void of danger, is yet an extremely inconvenient and distressing infirmity. Youth and old age are peculiarly liable to it. In some weakly boys it has continued from their infancy almost to the age of puberty; but much longer in girls, and in many more of them, and such who seemed in all other respects healthy. Females in general are more apt to have their urine pass away; so that laughing, or coughing, will more frequently force some of it from them, than from men; and some women, without any ill health, have all their lives had no power to retain their water. It is therefore a less alarming symptom in dangerous illnesses of women, than of men. Among the morbid causes of incontinence of urine may be reckoned all disorders of the urinary passages, the cutting for the stone, or the extraction of it by dilating the urethra, difficult labours, a prolapsus vaginæ, Venereal injuries, epileptic and paralytic affections, and whatever else can bring on extreme weakness in general, or of the urinary parts in particular.

A decoction of the Peruvian bark, and cold bathing, may be of some use in restoring more expeditiously the general strength after any illness, and so far contribute to remedy this infirmity; a blister may also be applied just above the os sacrum, in order to stimulate more particularly the parts concerned in retaining the urine. Where these have no effect, either time alone must cure the complaint, or it must be considered as incurable; in which case, for the use of males, a yoke has been contrived, which by means of a screw compresses the urethra, and hinders the dripping of the water. I have known several try this contrivance, but they found it so inconvenient, that they soon laid it aside. Some in its room have substituted a bladder, in which the penis was constantly kept in the day-time: this may be less cumbersome, but is not so neat as a tin vessel, which others have used for the same purpose. The most effectual way of keeping the bed dry, is to put the penis and scrotum into a small chamber-pot, and to keep them in this situation all night. A little practice has made this method easy to several persons, who have preferred it to all others.

Urine made of a deep coffee colour, or manifestly mixed with a large quantity of blood, has within my experience very rarely been the effect of any thing but a stone in the urinary passages. I therefore suppose a strong probability of this cause, wherever I see this appearance; and if there be joined with it any of the usual symptoms of the stone, I have no further doubts. A very painful strangury from the internal or external use of cantharides, has seldom, if ever, gone beyond making a slight redness of the water, with some few streaks of blood in the mucus.

A scirrhous prostate gland, when it becomes ulcerated, has occasioned some blood in the urine; but the quantity is very small, and is not increased by riding or walking; and whenever this is the cause, a surgeon by examining can hardly fail to discover it by the swelling and hardness. Cancerous sores communicating with any part of the urinary passages, may tinge the urine with blood; but these too may be conjectured from the constancy of the pains, from the small quantity of blood, from its not being remarkably increased upon motion, from the

fetid mucus, or sanies, which issues from them,
as well as from their wanting several peculiar
signs of the presence of a stone.

A blow upon the loins has appeared to occasion bloody urine; and I suppose a blood vessel
may happen to burst in the kidneys, or bladder, not only from such a violent cause, but
from as slight an one as it often does in the
nose; though I do not remember such an instance. But I have once or twice known a very
profuse bleeding into the urethra from some of
the neighbouring vessels, without any previous
distemper, or extraordinary injury of the part:
the blood kept constantly running out without
any effort to make water, and without its being
in the person's power to check it. In one of
these cases the bleeding returned frequently for
two years, during which time the health was
gradually impaired, and at the end of the
second year the patient died: the grumes of
blood were often voided with difficulty, and
occasioned great distress.

In the worst kinds of small-pox the blood is
well known to pour out from the urinary passages, as well as from other parts, in great
abundance.

Many other causes of bloody urine are to be
found in medical writers, which, if they exist,

have never occurred in my practice. Quiet,
and keeping the body cool, and open, are all
the means of relief, with which I am acquainted.

CHAP. 102.

Uterus.

A PROLAPSUS of the vagina or womb is only
to be relieved by a pessary: it is apt to be attended with an incontinence of urine.

Several women have experienced a sudden
and great discharge of water from their wombs;
this has happened to the same woman more
than once, and about the time of the menstrua
taking their final leave. No ill consequences
have followed this appearance, besides weakness.

There has grown out from the womb a fleshy
substance like a pear, the body of it being
much larger than the stalk. This has extended
itself so as to be perceivable in the vagina in
straining upon going to stool. The great evil
arising from this, is a constant discharge of blood
from the dilated parts, which discharge will
necessarily continue till the excrescence be
removed. An experienced accoucheur assured
me that he had taken away near twenty of

these by passing a ligature as near as possible to the part adhering to the womb: in a few days after this has been done, the mass falls off, and the remaining stalk putrefies away, requiring nothing but frequent injections of an infusion of chamomile flowers. He told me this operation had been generally successful; and it has proved so, where I have known it performed.

The furor uterinus does not always arise from a preternatural state of the womb, but, sometimes at least, differs not from common madness; the mind no longer under the guidance of reason, is made a prey to such thoughts as work it up to the œstrum Venereum, instead of those which might inflame it with religious zeal, ambition, or a desire of revenge. I have seen it not only in the young and middle-aged, but in a dying old woman, who had long been in a broken state of health, from which circumstances, as well as from the decency of her character, it may be judged that all delight in the objects upon which she raved, had been long passed and forgotten. Besides, it happens sometimes to the other sex, that madness lets loose the passion of lust, as well as those of fear, or anger.

The womb, as well as the breasts of women, is subject to scirrhous tumors, which slowly turn to incurable ulcers. This happens at the same time of life with similar disorders of the breasts, that is, generally after the age of forty. The first symptom is often a return of the menstrual discharge after it had long ceased: but this is no certain sign; for its reappearance has sometimes proceeded from other causes *, as well as from a scirrhous state of the womb. In some women the first alarm is given by a copious discharge of a tenacious mucus-like jelly, or of a thinner fluid, like the fluor albus: this has continued for one or two years, intermixed now and then with a discharge of blood, before any of the more violent symptoms have come on. These are, pains of the womb, in the groin, in the loins, in one or both of the hips, and in the thighs; pains in going to stool, and in making water, with a tenesmus, and a frequent call to make water, a manifest fulness of the abdomen, and at the same time a sense of emptiness, and a hectic fever. The discharge afterwards becomes yellow, green, or black, and fetid; and the pains are so excessive, as hardly to be endured without benumbing the sense of them in some degree by large quantities of opium. They are scarcely increased by the motion of a

---

* See chap. 62.

carriage. In a few cases the ulcer of the womb has eaten a passage to the bladder, and to the rectum. All these symptoms do not happen in every case; but a very few of them are sufficient to shew the nature of the disease, even before it has been ascertained by a midwife's examination of the womb.

The extract of hemlock washed down with a decoction of the Peruvian bark is at least innocent in this disorder; but I have had very little reason to judge this, or any other medicine, to be of much avail in curing, or checking the progress of the cancer. One woman was very remarkably relieved, while she was taking the extract, and at the same time using an injection of the decoction of hemlock; the pains almost vanished, and the womb remained in such a quiet state for some years, as to give very little interruption to her usual amusements, or manner of living. But in most other cases no good could be done, but by administering in a proper manner some preparation of opium.

THE CONCLUSION.

It might be expected, that the experience of fifty years spent in the practice of Physic would have taught me more, than I here appear to have learned, of distempers, and their remedies. I readily confess my knowledge of them to be slight, and imperfect; and that a considerable share of this imperfection is chargeable upon my want of ability to make a better use of the opportunities I have had: but at the same time it must be allowed, that some part must be put down to the very great difficulty of making improvements in the medical art. This is too evident from the slow progress, which has been made, though men well qualified by their learning, experience, and abilities, have for above two thousand years been communicating to the world all they could add by just reasoning to the facts collected by attentive observation. Whoever applies himself to the study of nature, must own we are yet greatly in the dark in regard even to brute matter, and that we know but little of the properties and powers of the inanimate creation: but we have all this darkness to perplex us in studying animated nature, and a great deal more arising from the unknown peculiarities of life; for to living bodies belong many additional powers, the operations of which can never be acco t- ed for by the laws of lifeless matter. The art of healing therefore has scarcely hitherto had any guide but the slow one of experience*, and has yet made no illustrious advances by the help of reason; nor will it probably make any, till Providence think fit to bless mankind by sending into the world some superior genius capable of contemplating the animated world with the sagacity shewn by Newton in the ina‑ nimate, and of discovering that great principle of life, upon which its existence depends, and by which all its functions are governed and directed.

* Ευριφων ὁ ιατρος εξωτηθεις τον διδασκαλον, παξ᾽ ᾧ επαιδευθη, παρα τῳ χρονῳ, εφη.   *Stobæi Eclog. Phys.* lib. i. pag. 19.

Printed by S. Hamilton, Falcon-Court, Fleet-Street.